THE
LAXDOELA SAGA

THE
LAXDOELA

SAGA

TRANSLATED
FROM THE
OLD ICELANDIC
WITH INTRODUCTION
AND NOTES
BY A. MARGARET ARENT

UNIVERSITY OF WASHINGTON PRESS   SEATTLE
THE AMERICAN-SCANDINAVIAN FOUNDATION   NEW YORK

Copyright © 1964 by the University of Washington Press

Library of Congress Catalog Card Number 63-20538

Printed in the United States of America

*To my parents
for
their unfailing love and support*

Preface

It was during an introductory course in Old Icelandic at the University of Chicago that this project was first envisioned. The work was first presented as part of a doctoral dissertation and has been considerably revised since then. The fact that the sagas were basically heathen in outlook and written in a palatable narrative prose gave them a unique position in early Germanic literature. To capture the matchless style of an Icelandic saga in English aroused my interest and presented something of a challenge. Such a challenge, I have found, can never be met to the complete satisfaction of the translator. It can only be hoped that some of the genius of the original author's creation will shine through. The process of translating, revising, polishing, seeking equivalent expressions has been in itself a reward to me. In some respects, however, a translation will forever remain an unfinished product, and should perhaps more than any other work rest a decade as prescribed by Horace, for "delere licebit, quod non edideris; nescit vox missa reverti" — "the unpublished may be deleted; but a word once uttered can never be revised."

Many scholars, friends, and institutions have contributed to the completion of the task, and I should like to acknowledge them here. To the City of Oslo I am indebted for an award to attend the Summer School Session of 1957 at the University of Olso, at which time I had the opportunity to become acquainted with the Nordic cultural past through instruction and visits at the museums in Oslo, Bergen, and Stockholm. The archaeological exhibits brought fresh insight into the arts, crafts, and cultural heritage of the Viking period. It was also possible for me to visit the Romsdal in Norway, the district from which the saga-age characters in the *Laxdoela Saga* emigrated.

To the United States Educational Foundation in Iceland (Fulbright) and to the Board of Foreign Scholarships I should like to express my gratitude for a fourteen-month study grant to Iceland in 1958-59. Without the advantage of a stay in Iceland the work could not have been successfully completed. Living in the linguistic and geographic environment that produced the sagas could not help but bring the literature alive and give inspiration to the work of re-creation, which a translation in some respects must be. Owing to its conservatism, modern Icelandic also proved an indispensable aid in the interpreting and correct rendering of the idiomatic language of the Old Icelandic. Long walks through the valleys around the Hvammsfjord, where I located all the saga sites and wandered about the farms, provided the real stage setting.

To the many Icelandic friends and scholars, to the officers at the United States Information Service — all of whom gave generously of their time and encouragement — I should like to extend my appreciation. My acceptance of the Fulbright grant and my prolonged stay in Iceland were made possible through the kind consent of Professor W. P. Lehmann and the administrative board of the University of Texas to grant me leave of absence.

Most especially I wish to express my thanks to Professors George J. Metcalf and Gösta Franzén of the University of Chicago for their patient and careful reading of the preliminary manuscript, and for their helpful criticisms. I am particularly indebted to Professor Franzén, who gave me the encouragement to set out on the long endeavor, and who was always willing to offer his assistance and suggestions.

For the rendering of the maps I owe grateful acknowledgment to my father, Mr. Lyn E. Arent, who has drawn them to scale, adapting and simplifying some of them from portions of the *Uppdráttur Íslands* (Geodætisk Institut, Copenhagen).

Contents

Illustrations

Introduction

Literary Background

WITH the Christianization of Iceland (A.D. 1000), a new era in the life and letters of the nation can be said to have begun, although the conversion was not marked by any great upheaval, politically or culturally. The old shaded off into the new and blended imperceptibly with it. The Church, which gradually brought the culture of southern Europe to Iceland, established schools, and taught the art of writing, did not squelch indigenous traditions, but rather served as the stimulus under which Icelandic letters developed to their height in the thirteenth century.

In this classical period, literary creativity burgeoned in Iceland, preserving poetic forms of the past and developing a new literary genre, the saga. The political scene, however, would seem to preclude this propitious endeavor, for Iceland at that time was in the throes of vindictive feuds and power struggles which sapped the nation's vitality and led to the forfeiture of independence. An age notorious for savageries and depravities of every sort thus also fostered Iceland's finest cultural achievement. The Sagas of Icelanders which were produced in this atmosphere depict the heyday of the Commonwealth, the days when Iceland enjoyed political autonomy and lived under a code of honor based on personal dignity and worth. It is perhaps not so puzzling that in the midst of moral and social disintegration there were those for whom the past loomed large in nostalgic reminiscence. On the one hand, as a kind of tribute to the heroic age of greatness, the sagas revitalized the past. On the other hand they combined the essential substance of the bygone days with the experience of contemporary developments. In this discrepancy between the cultural reference and the cultural context lies some of the fascination and enigma of the saga literature.

Iceland was settled late in the ninth century. The emigration from Norway, undertaken by many of the chieftains and petty kings to escape the domination of King Harald Fairhair, marked the last of the major movements of the Viking period. Iceland enjoyed home rule until 1262 when it fell under the Norwegian Crown. In the founding days, the sovereign power lay in the hands of the *goðar*, chieftain-priests who fulfilled both political and religious functions. A *goði*'s authority (pl. *goðar*) extended over those who paid dues and worshiped at his temple. In exchange for this privilege and the *goði*'s protection, these followers pledged him their allegiance and support. These quite naturally were the farmers and neighbors in his immediate vicinity. The number of *goðar* was limited, and the title was generally hereditary. The farmers reserved the right to choose the *goði* whom they wished to follow, but loyalty to a certain one usually became more or less habitual. The relationship was thus one of mutual trust and agreement — the old Germanic code of loyalty between chieftain and followers.

The years of the Commonwealth saw the establishment of the Althing (A.D. 930), a democratic parliament with a strong aristocratic base. The *goðar* automatically became members of the ruling bodies of parliament (the legislature and the judicature), and a Lawspeaker was elected to recite the laws at the meeting of the Althing which took place once a year on the plains of Thingvellir in the southwest of the country. As time went on, the *goði*'s obligations became more political than religious, his power territorial. There was no centralized authority over and above the *goðar* — a weakness in the political structure which left much leeway for internal feuds and later led to power politics and personal aggrandizement.

The old moral order had rested on a sense of personal dignity, honor, and loyalty, and on obligations of kinship. Any injury to one's honor or that of one's kin demanded payment, in blood or money. Theoretically justice was a meting out in kind, like for like, wergild for wergild, one killing for another. In the weighing and balancing of just deserts, a man's worth and station were taken into account. The

equalizing of damages, compensation, arbitration, and mutual agreement were self-imposed codes, respected and carried out with a sense
of responsibility. The fact that the courts were not empowered to
carry out sentence was another inherent weakness, however, which
not only condoned but encouraged the taking of the law into one's
own hands. Outlawry, fines, and settlements had to be enforced by
the plaintiff.

The petty slights and insults to one's honor which occasioned bloody
revenge and internecine feuds seem exaggerated and pathetic by
present-day standards, yet these were the codes by which men lived,
passionately at times, and violently. Justice did not necessarily pre-
suppose killings; there were peaceable men who strove to settle differ-
ences in a way that would do both sides honor without the spilling of
blood. But it is the other alternative that most captivated the minds of
the saga authors, and it is no wonder that they readily saw a parallel
in the contemporary scene where vendettas and indiscriminate blood-
shed were the order of the day. The honorable code of justice had re-
coiled upon itself, like the snake swallowing its own tail.

The Icelanders, as their Scandinavian forebears, were polytheistic,
although worship of the gods was rather haphazard and had been on
the wane throughout the tenth century. The individual therefore was
more apt to rely on himself, placing his trust in his own weapons and
strength (chapter 40). Superstitious belief in portents, omens, dreams,
fetches, and visions of second sight, however, found widespread acceptance. Along with this, the conviction prevailed that life was
ruled by an inscrutable destiny, a fatalism that manifested itself in
the fortune or misfortunes of individual lives, but which ultimately
pervaded all life as a nemesis and sickness at the core, a doomsday
from which there was no escape. Christianity could do little to eradi-
cate these deep-seated convictions. Substituting one God for a plural-
ity in whom the people had little faith to begin with is minor compared with any unseating of these more diffuse beliefs which are part
of the soul of the folk. It is understandable, too, that this fatalistic
belief was readily amalgamated with the Biblical conception of the
end of the world and apocryphal omens (cf. the "Vǫluspá" in the
Edda). Thangbrand, after an unsuccessful attempt to convert the
Icelanders, returned to Norway and reported to what a sorry pass his

mission had come, saying that "to his mind Christianity would never take root in Iceland" (chapter 41).

To some of the more perceptive authors of the day, the fateful destiny toward which the nation was headed in the thirteenth century must also have presented a visible parallel to the age-old belief in fate. In some ways it must have seemed like a fulfillment of a chain of causes begun in the past, a snowballing of the consequences of an ethical system that demanded equal revenge, linking disaster to disaster. What had been present from the beginning in germ was now coming to fruition.

At the beginning of the Christian period, Iceland came under the diocese of Bremen, and the influence of the Church was limited. Native Icelanders traveled and were educated abroad; many became bishops in the new church at home. The great distance from Rome, the loose ties with Bremen, and the independent spirit of the Icelanders hampered any real domination by the Church. Men of high rank, the *goðar* and their sons, reinforced their authority and titles by serving the Church as priests and clerics. The bishops held seats in parliament; celibacy was never successfully enforced among the clergy. Thus here again in the early days of the Church there was no sharp demarcation between ecclesiastical and secular functions. Those schooled under Holy Church were men of the world, secular in outlook and interests. They learned to write under monastic guidance, but what they wrote reflected their own life and culture, their nation's spirit, and their national language.

The Commonwealth was a way of life which had deep roots in the past. It was conservative, even reactionary, tenaciously clinging to the values, traditions, and language of the homeland—a trait not uncommon to a people that has emigrated. They had brought with them a heritage of poetry—mythological and heroic lays that lived on in oral tradition and were later collected and written down in the *Edda* (*ca.* 1270). They had particularly gifted poets, the scalds, whose verses have been preserved in many of the sagas; and they no doubt brought along with them the innate desire and ability for storytelling, common to remote and primitive peoples in the preliterate stage.

The craft of writing is usually first exercised on the applied arts, and this too was the case in Iceland. The recording of the laws, translations of didactic religious works, the lives of saints, and the like paved the way for proficiency in narrative expression. A predilection for secular topics, however, apart from the laws, early made itself apparent. There had always been a lively interest in heritage and genealogy since most of the families in Iceland could trace their origin back to kingships and the nobility in Norway. Thus the Icelanders in the eleventh and twelfth centuries committed to parchment works concerning their ancestors, the Settlement of Iceland, and accounts of its Christianization. From the beginning they seemed to have had a sense for history and their place in it. Among some of these early works there is Sæmundr the Wise's *History of the Kings of Norway*, Ari Thorgilsson's *Íslendingabók*, and the *Landnámabók* (The Book of the Settlement, a compilation of the names of the first settlers, their ancestors and descendants, with brief biographical sketches).

When one considers that the most popular and striking figure of the day, King Óláf Haraldsson (died 1030), was both king and saint, the transition from writing saints' lives to Kings' Sagas is quite understandable. The so-called *First Saga of Saint Óláf* was probably written around 1180. About ten years later, Oddr Snorrason wrote a saga about King Óláf Tryggvason, the king who Christianized Norway and Iceland. (Both of these kings figure as prominent characters in the *Laxdoela saga*, cf. chapters 40 and 73.) Both Sæmundr and Oddr wrote their works in Latin, but they were so soon translated into the vernacular that we know them only in that form.

In 1190 the diocese under whose jurisdiction Iceland fell was changed from Bremen to Trondheim. Iceland was thus drawn into the religious and political orbit of Norway. At this time it was decreed that no *goðar* could be ordained unless they renounced their secular title. Although this brought about a clearer separation of Church and State, along with it came tighter control by the Church and closer ties with the Crown in Norway. Bonds with the mother country had never been entirely broken — Icelandic scalds had long been court favorites and there had always been those who sought honor abroad. Now, however, increasing numbers of prominent Icelanders became liegemen to the king, relinquishing more and more their national independence for personal gain.

By this time, however, writers and clerics had become sufficiently exercised in written expression that a lay literature could develop independently of the Church. The Kings' Sagas gradually shed their hagiographic tinge. Snorri Sturluson, who put his stamp on the age of the Sturlungs (1200-62), had not learned Latin. In his *Heimskringla* (Orb of the World), he recast the Kings' Sagas into a lively and realistic narrative. With contemporary events drawing Iceland into ever closer relationship with Norway, it was natural that authors should turn to recording these connections and tracing the continuity with the mother country. Snorri, and in all likelihood many of the anonymous contemporary writers, was not a mere observer but an active participant in the events of his time.

Like the Kings' Sagas, the Sagas of Icelanders (or Family Sagas) also reflect the genealogical and historical interest of those times. In presentation and form they resemble the Kings' Sagas; in subject matter they too draw on •historical material — primarily the lives of Icelanders during the days of the Settlement, but also on the common cultural heritage, legal and religious customs. But these sagas were composed with something else in mind than chronicles, family histories, or documentation, and they rely to varying degrees on historical facts. The authors have formed and organized their material into something more than esthetically pleasing history. The best of them are unified wholes, their structures ordered toward symbolizing an idea in esthetic form. The apex of the period brought forth among others *Egils saga, Eyrbyggja saga, Laxdoela saga,* and *Njáls saga.* Despite a certain solidarity of style and similarity of theme and handling, each one will be found unique. Though anonymous, the perceptiveness and predilection of individual authors can usually be detected. They use common themes and devices to suit their own ends, exhibit varying degrees of mastery over their material, and handle their historical sources with greater or less freedom. At such an early stage in the history of European literatures, these sagas boast a narrative style that rings surprisingly modern in contrast to the courtly romances and epic verse forms of contemporary medieval Europe.

Manuscripts, Date, and Authorship

The *Laxdoela saga* is a fine representative of the saga genre created in Iceland in the thirteenth century. The English equivalent of
its title would read: *The Saga of the Laxdalers*. It is both a regional
and a family saga. The Laxdalers were the settlers and inhabitants
of the Laxárdal, a valley on the western coast of Iceland in the district
Dalasýsla at the head of the Hvammsfjord (cf. map).

Two classes of manuscripts are extant from which we know the
story. We are indeed fortunate in having the text whole or in part
on six vellums, for in general a vellum is to be preferred over paper
copies. The Y-class vellums include a sequel to the story, the *Bolla
þáttr*. There are two complete Y-class vellums that are independent of
one another and thus serve as excellent control for editions made
from this class. The most famous manuscript of this class is the
Möðruvallabók. It is a parchment of two hundred leaves from the
first half of the fourteenth century and contains eleven sagas, of
which *Laxdoela* is the tenth in the series.

The Z-class MSS are older and would be preferred, except for the
fact that they are all fragmentary. The oldest of these (D_2) has been
dated *ca.* 1250. Thus the saga must be at least that old, and some
think it likely that this fragment (luckily salvaged from a bookbind-
ing) may even be the archetype of the text.

Internal evidence corroborates this dating of the saga. The genealogies in the saga lead both backward and forward. The latter frequently include the names of bishops and priests who lived beyond the
frame of the story and take us into the time of composition. The dates
of many of these personages are known from church records. A
terminus a quo can be derived from the mention of Thorvald
Snorrason who died in 1228 (chapter 31). The arrival of Unn in
Iceland can be set fairly close to the date 892. (The first permanent
settler arrived in 874.) Saint Óláf's death (1030) is mentioned
shortly before the end of the saga. The events of the story proper
cover then a period of approximately one hundred and fifty years from
the ninth into the eleventh century (*ca.* 892-1030). Roughly one
hundred and eighty to two hundred years had thus elapsed between
the last events described in the saga (1030) and the composition of

the work (sometime after 1228). One might naturally expect that scribes tended to interpolate names bringing the story up to their own time, but there is sufficient evidence that this has not been the case in *Laxdoela*.

The consciousness of the time discrepancy is evident in the author's expressions contrasting the "then" and "now." The mention of the ordeal of "going-under-the-sod" (chapter 18) — which was taken just as seriously by the heathen as "Christian men do *now* [italics mine] when such ordeals are performed" — leads to external evidence that helps narrow down the possible date of the saga. Ordeals were abolished by Cardinal William of Sabena in Norway in 1247, and mention is made in the Icelandic annals of such a change in ordinance in 1248.

Anachronisms in the text such as insignia on shields, the use of courtly words (*riddari*, "knight"; *glaðel*, "lance"; *kurteisi*, "courtoisie"), and the obvious fascination of the author with ostentation and dress point to the influence of the southern romances in the author's own day. Translations of them had begun with Friar Robert's *Tristans saga* in Norway in 1226, and these romances with their courtly ideals began filtrating into Iceland around 1240-50.

Echoes of contemporary accounts found in the *Sturlunga saga* (a composite of many sagas and *þættir* [shorter tales] composed in the thirteenth century about contemporary events and taken to be reliable accounts) have been noted in *Laxdoela* by Rolf Heller and others.[1] Two events in particular aid in dating *Laxdoela*. The *Deildartungumál* (a famous legal case mentioned in the *Sturlu saga* in the *Sturlunga saga*) concerns the succession to inheritance in a family that perished in a single shipwreck about 1178. The drowning of Thorstein Surt (*Laxdoela*, chapter 18) seems to be patterned after the contemporary event. There is not even a hint in the *Landnámabók* or other sources that Thorstein drowned at all. Either *Laxdoela*'s author has assimilated material still within memory of his day or actually knew the *Sturlu saga*, and this is not at all inconceivable since it was probably written early in the thirteenth century and in the same district as *Laxdoela*.

Another incident from contemporary times which the saga author likely incorported occurs in *Þórðar saga kakala* in the *Sturlunga saga:* "Then his wife Vigdís Markúsdóttir came up. Ásbjorn dried his bloody sword on her clothes."[2] In 1244 Ásbjorn Gudmundarson went with some men to Húnavatnssýsla on this mission. If the author has indeed utilized this episode in the passage where Helgi Hard-beinsson wipes his bloody spear on Gudrún's fine attire (*Laxdoela,* chapter 55) — suiting the deed to be sure to his own purpose — then *Laxdoela* must have been written after 1244 and rather soon after.

Laxdoela saga is mentioned by name in other sagas, the earliest reference being in the *Eyrbyggja saga,* which has been dated around 1250. Thus it is reasonable to assume that *Laxdoela* was composed between 1228 and 1250, and likely between 1244 and 1248.

Conjectures about the author and place of composition continue to occupy the imagination of many. It has been assumed from geographic orientations within the saga that the place of composition must have been in the local district around the Hvammsfjord, and the favored localities are the two prominent settlements at Helgafell and Hjardar-holt. It is probable that the author was a cleric, but all attempts to ascertain his name have been futile.

Sources and Origins

As for the substance of the narrative, we are undeniably presented with echoes from the *Landnámabók,*[3] from the poetic *Edda,*[4] from other sagas, and from contemporary accounts found in the *Sturlunga saga.* Thus we find an amazing amalgamation of material old and new. Evidence of these influences and interdependencies throws light on the author's acquaintance with both the oral and written traditions of his time, but the parallels can by no means be called slavish bor-rowings. Many of the motifs are so common that proof of actual influence from one saga to another cannot be established with any certainty. And in those cases where the parallels seem obvious and striking, the author of *Laxdoela* has made something entirely his own out of them.

It has long been a debatable issue how much of the substance of the Family Sagas has come down from oral tradition. What sort of tales were told in the preliterate period we can only guess; how much of them went into the Family Sagas will forever remain unknown.

Naturally an indigenous facility in oral storytelling precedes any literate age of poetry, and although reflexes of the former oral techniques are without a doubt discernible in the transitional literature of an early lettered age, these oral devices will continue to be drawn upon only as long as they serve the purposes of the new medium, where they have become, properly speaking, *literary* devices. It must be remembered, too, that a real connection between oral presentation and written literature did exist at the time of the composition of the sagas, for they were meant to be read aloud.

There are many indications that point to a teller-to-audience directive: "Now let us return to Iceland and see what has been going on there since Thorkel went away" (chapter 58), or the perfunctory announcement of a newcomer to the saga: "There was a man by the name of...." Oral clichés such as "people say," "that is the talk of people," and so forth are found on nearly every page. It is not surprising that a written story should now properly seem to be a told story. But there are signs that the techniques are already on the verge of becoming hackneyed and outworn. The important thing, as far as the author's sources are concerned, is that oral technique be distinguished from the handing down of the content of the story. The author has drawn on all of his experience — the literature he knew, the historical material available to him, a form of presentation accepted and familiar in his day, episodes from contemporary events — and transformed them in his own creative imagination to suit his master design.

Historical Reliability

Coupled with the issue of the oral saga is the problem of historical reliability. The Free-prosaists, as the advocates of an oral origin are called, assert not only that oral sagas preceded the written works as a substratum but that these sagas were passed down from the time of the events and were thus reliable accounts even to the individual dialogues. This theory has persisted with modifications and concessions down to the present century.[5] In 1949 Sigurdur Nordal dealt a devastating blow to this theory with his *Hrafnkatla*,[6] in which he demonstrated conclusively that the characters and story of *Hrafnkels saga* are fictitious and that realistic prose can in fact present a semblance of reality so convincing that it has taken scholarship centuries to recognize the genius of the saga authors. The Free-prosaists had always been hard pressed in their argument for an oral folk tradition in free prose that could transmit through centuries historically accurate accounts. The mental arabesques and exceptions required to make the theory plausible have had to yield to more cogent arguments. Several factors contributed to the almost fanatic desire on part of the older generation of scholars and laymen in general to salvage the venerable age and truthfulness of the sagas: (1) The saga literature was discovered at the beginning of the seventeenth century, a time when national interests in Scandinavia ran high. Each nation vied with the other in obtaining the valuable codices, and each sought to find in them proof of a past grandeur. Even the mythological sagas were taken as bona fide history, and the Kings' Sagas and Family Sagas were naturally taken at face value. Some of this "belief" in the sagas continues to the present day. (2) Especially in the case of the Family Sagas it seemed obvious that the accounts were reliable — most of the characters could be attested and were known to have lived; the genealogies in the main were accurate; the time and setting were real; the farmsteads stand today in their original places with the names of their owners of a thousand years ago. (3) Since the Family Sagas went back to the time of the events, they were felt to have preceded the composition of the Kings' Sagas. Nordal has argued for a reversal of the chronology — the Family Sagas begin with biographical sagas of scalds who were court poets in Norway. These sagas then are a transition from the Kings' Sagas, both in content and form. The Kings' Sagas made use of scaldic verses as sources for the facts and episodes about the kings, and the verses were incorporated into the sagas. In sagas about scalds, their verses were naturally part of the narrative. Thus it came to be assumed that verses in a saga indicated authenticity of the content. In the Family Sagas these could then very well be invented to give the appearance of valid tradition and verification. From time immemorial the poet has captured his audience by appealing to the credibility of his tale. It is therefore not to be wondered at that the saga authors would want their stories to seem true. The devices they used to create the illusion are discussed below, pp. xxxviii-xxxix. (4)

The direct narrative prose and dialogue were naïvely taken at face value as discursive language and oral recounting. Critics failed to consider the possibility of artistic semblance and the poetic use of language, especially in free prose.

According to the various conjectures concerning the oral origin of the sagas, they were deemed more or less historical. Some Free-prosaists assumed that the sagas were amalgamations of separate parts — the *þættir* theory. These *þættir* were collected and put together by a redactor or scribe. The more a saga exhibited a unity of structure, the more changes it had undergone, the more it deviated in other words from its original purity and genuineness. Thus unity of composition came to be a decisive factor in the arguments of oral *vs.* written, of fact *vs.* fiction.

The Book-prosaists, as the opposition school is called, place greater emphasis on the artistic nature of the sagas and assign them to the literate period — they are written works of artistic merit, composed by individual authors, who succeeded to varying degrees in unifying their subject matter. The Book-prosaists argued that unity could only be attributable to an author who could view his work as a whole, and that the masterful handling of the materials pointed to a written tradition. Paradoxically, the most radical of the Free-prosaists insisted that the oral tradition could account for everything, both historical reliability and artistic excellence — the earliest sagas, closest to the oral tradition, were the most perfect as compositions, and also the most accurate.

National and romantic interests, wishful thinking, and disregard for adjacent disciplines prevented more objective discrimination. Nordal has shown that the literary endeavors in Iceland do indeed follow an ascending gradient — the best compositions are the latest — and that there are many inaccuracies and deviations from strict historical fact. Scholars are now beginning to ferret out the relationships between sagas, the influences from the thirteenth-century *Sturlunga saga,* and see the Family Sagas as compositions of individual writers. All of these findings would seem to indicate that the Book-prosaists have won the day. Even the Kings' Sagas can no longer satisfy the requirements of the historical disciplines. It is thus reasonable to concede that the Family Sagas are primarily works of art and belong to the literary discipline, which does not deny that they have a basis in real life, real persons, and events. Yet what the author has made of the cultural and historical material is not history.

In the case of the *Laxdoela saga* specifically, it has been sufficiently demonstrated that the author has created some fictitious characters and scenes, that the chronology cannot bear too close scrutiny, and that the position of Icelanders abroad is obviously enhanced beyond strict fact. As examples of the cases in point, I might just mention that the genealogy of Óláf the White is confused, that Thorbjorn Skrjúp and his son Lambi are otherwise unattested, that the Mýrkjartan and Melkorka episodes seem to have been invented for the purpose of the story, and that the Helgi Hardbeinsson scene has no historical basis. The main disruption of historical time occurs when young Bolli Bollason appears in the story as a lad of twelve years (chapter 59). No reader who is participating in the illusion of the story, however, would even be aware that a chronological shift, measured by historical time outside the story, had occurred. It is the author's poetic end that justifies the manipulation. The superlative descriptions of the reception of Icelanders abroad in their stereotyped formulations are obvious exaggerations. That Bolli Bollason was the first to be in the Varangian Guard is chronologically impossible (chapter 76).

While comparisons with historical facts, correlation with real time outside the story, sifting of fact from fiction, ferreting out influences and origins are interesting in themselves, such studies do little to illuminate the author's intent in creating the work. Analyses extraneous to the work can only succeed in diverting attention from the work as a whole and as it stands before us. Recent investigations into the sources and materials used by the author rather give the impression of a patching together of fragments from here and there — not much different from the piecing together of *þættir*, only that now the pieces are from written literature rather than oral traditions. Reducing the end product to all its elements cannot satisfactorily explain its art form and organic unity, for it is more than the sum of its parts. Whatever the origin of technique and substance, whatever prompted the conception in the author's mind, all of it has been rewoven in the author's formative imagination, emerging as a totally new and felicitous creation.

Summary of the Plot

According to the story, Ketil Flatnose, a chieftain in Norway, together with his children and kinsmen, set sail from the homeland in the latter decades of the ninth century. Ketil settled in Scotland, his daughter Unn the Deep-minded in the Breidafjord Dales in Iceland. She claimed all the lands around the head of the Hvammsfjord, including the Laxárdal (literally meaning the "Salmon River Valley," cf. map). Her brother Bjorn the Eastman also settled in Iceland in the Breidafjord District. The saga sets forth an account of the generations descending from Unn and Bjorn.

The story falls into three interlocking parts. The first or prelude (chapters 1-31) takes up almost half of the book, and the saga has often been criticized for its lengthy introduction. There is such a multiplication of characters and episodes that the reader may feel he is getting nowhere with the plot. These many colorful characters and unforgettable episodes are like vignettes that can be enjoyed in themselves. But upon closer reading, each of these scenes will be found to be subordinate to the whole design, slowly but surely laying the foundation for what is to come, injecting an element that forms the node for the next link in the chain of action.

It is by no means easy to give a straightforward account of the plot in this first section, for although a thread follows the succeeding generations and leads to a culmination, the reader is constantly called upon to relate back and forth, picking up threads that have been temporarily dropped, comparing and substantiating what he has heard before. The movement is not strictly cumulative, gaining momentum to the end. The sweeping dramatic impulse, once begun, is offset by a leisurely epic pace. The action halts at intervals, introducing yet another character and episode, reflecting back, rounding out what has been prepared and hinted.

Generation after generation of Unn's side of the house marches past, each successive one perhaps a bit more illustrious than the former. There are quarrels, disagreements, and battles among the kinsmen, but all with their temporary assuaging of ill feelings. The characters and situations prepare the reader for the same types of themes in the central action, laying before him a mural of the saga world and accustoming him to the social and moral ordering of that world. The characters we meet have some of the stuff in them that makes the main characters what they are — Óláf Feilan, Hoskuld, Óláf Peacock — all have in them something of a Kjartan, the hero of the story. Unn, Jórunn, Vigdís, Melkorka are not so much different from Gudrún, the heroine of the main theme.

It might perhaps be useful to the reader to give some glimpses in preview so that the rambling and diversified introduction may take on continuity with the main theme. Unn, the matriarch of the family, sets the tone for the story, planning wise marriages, generously parceling out her land claim, and keeping her dignity to the end. The plot moves forward with the birth of Hoskuld, Unn's great-great-grandson, one of the most illustrious figures in the saga. He journeys abroad and purchases a concubine. With a few masterful strokes, the author sets before us the brightly colored tent of Gilli with the twelve concubines behind the curtain, Hoskuld's transactions with Gilli, and the weighing of the purse. Then we catch a glimpse of this rare beauty whom Hoskuld has bought for three times the price of an ordinary bondwoman. It turns out that she is the daughter of the Irish King Mýrkjartan. She gives birth to a son by Hoskuld, who is Óláf Peacock, the father of Kjartan.

Before Óláf's career is launched with the claiming of his royal pedigree and the wooing of his bride, the saga takes time to introduce us to the neighbors of Hoskuld. The story of Hrapp, his haunted farm, and ghost walkings holds our interest through many chapters. Other neighbors of Hrapp and Hoskuld are Thórd Goddi and Vigdís. The two of them get involved in the sheltering of an outlaw, as a result of which Vigdís divorces Thórd, who is then forced to give over all his property to Hoskuld and to foster Hoskuld's son Óláf. After Hoskuld's death Óláf and his half brothers Thorleik and Bárd divide the paternal inheritance in thirds, much to the discontent of Thorleik. The argument between Óláf and Thorleik is settled when Óláf offers to foster Thorleik's son Bolli (Thorleiksson), by which time Óláf's own son Kjartan has been born to him out of his marriage with

Thorgerd Egilsdóttir. The coming together of the foster brothers Kjartan and Bolli brings the generations to a culmination. With the extraordinary prowess and accomplishments of these brilliant and gallant lads the prelude comes to a happy close.

The main theme (chapters 32-56) is sounded with the entrance of the other side of Ketil's house into the saga — Gudrún and her father Ósvíf, the descendants of Bjorn the Eastman (cf. chart). Essentially this main theme relates a tragedy in the personal lives of Kjartan, Bolli, and Gudrún, who are bound together in love and friendship, but for whom fate has preordained hatred and killings. It is a tale of a love triangle with all its subterfuges, vicious insinuations, retaliations, and heartaches, presented with the detachment and subtle discernment so typical of the sagas.

Chapters 32-33 serve as an interlude, setting the stage for all the subsequent action. In these two chapters the prophetic statements of Gest (the prophet-seer par excellence in the saga) follow one upon the other in rapid succession. From here on the plot is easy to follow for it is a denouement of what has been predicted. Kjartan's life and death hang by two swords that come into the family — the one, Footbite, owned first by the scoundrel Geirmund and later by Bolli, has a curse on it that will be the death of that member in the family hardest to lose. The sword Konungsnaut, a gift of the king to Kjartan, carries with it a protective blessing. Through the curse and the blessing the two swords are juxtaposed, their powers pitted one against the other. Gest predicts that Bolli will "stand over Kjartan's crown and thereby reap his own death." The antagonism between the foster brothers arises over their love for Gudrún.

Gudrún Ósvífsdóttir — high-spirited, strikingly beautiful, sharptongued, witty, proud, vain, ambitious, fiercely jealous, calculating, and unrelenting in venting her hurt pride — directly and indirectly instigates the death of her two lovers. Her life is laid before her in four dreams, foretelling her four marriages. Lifted from the context all these previews of the lives of Kjartan, Bolli, and Gudrún provide the scaffolding for the remainder of the saga. Subordinate premonitions and hints throughout the narrative substantiate and strengthen the inevitability of their fates. The suspense is not based on ignorance, but on the incompletion of a foreknown completion. What is so fascinating about the story is thus to watch and see how the natural involvements of the characters and the demands of the moral code of revenge play hand in hand with what fate has already predicted.

After the fulfillment of Gudrún's first two marriages, which are full of exciting and amusing episodes, we are told of the friendship between the house of Óláf and the house of Ósvíf — a bond which is strengthened by the close friendship of the three young people. It is here that the fates of Kjartan and Bolli become intertwined with that of Gudrún in the fulfillment of her third dream.

Óláf, prescient and cautious, has premonitions of the impending breach between the two families. But Kjartan, unheedful of his father's foreboding, continues to frequent the hot spring at Laugar where he and Gudrún can enjoy each other's company. Bolli always goes along, and it is not hard to guess that he may secretly be nurturing an affection for Gudrún, despite the fact that the author has camouflaged it under the foster brothers' habit of always being together — "no matter where they went."

Kjartan — impetuous, gallant, eager for fame and glory — hastily decides to journey abroad, leaving Gudrún behind. Kjartan and Bolli, their friendship unimpaired, journey together to Norway, where the rivalry between them first flares to the surface. The ruffled feelings and undercurrent of envy on Bolli's part remain subdued and controlled while attention is turned to another problem. The king of Norway has been exerting pressure on the heathen to accept the new religion. During the altercations in the Christianizing of Iceland, Kjartan is held hostage, whereas Bolli is permitted to sail for home.

Upon his arrival, Bolli loses no time in paying court to Gudrún and wins her hand, much to the dismay of his foster father Óláf. Snatching the bride is the feather in his cap that bolsters his pride. The motives are nowhere made explicit; Bolli himself would be the first to deny that he deliberately acted against his foster brother.

Upon Kjartan's return, the interplay of emotions, the fury of passion and resentment are at first restrained, only to break through periodically in whiplash insinuations or be repressed in poignant silences. But the pent-up emotions cannot be contained for long.

Three festive parties harbor the seeds of hatred and revenge. At the first one Kjartan refuses Bolli's gift of a stud of horses. Subsequently he marries the sweet and gentle Hrefna, the very opposite in temperament to Gudrún. At the next party, Gudrún, who can scarcely suppress her jealousy, inveigles Hrefna into letting her see the fabulous headdress which Kjartan had brought from Norway and which had been meant for her, Gudrún, as a wedding gift. It is touching to see how the guileless Hrefna obliges Gudrún, taking her to the storehouse where it is safely kept in a chest. Slowly unfolding it, Gudrún has not a word to say — her reticence expresses more than any words could. When the party ends, the sword Konungsnaut is stolen by Gudrún's brothers. It is recovered, but without its scabbard, so that Kjartan never carries it again. The protective sword will thus not be ready when Kjartan needs it most.

At the third party, Hrefna's expensive headdress disappears, never to be found again. Now the breach is irreparable; hostilities and spiteful acts ensue until Gudrún finally eggs Bolli on into killing Kjartan. Bolli regretfully draws the sword Footbite and the first part of Gest's prophecy is fulfilled.

After the peaceful Óláf dies, Kjartan's mother and brothers take up the revenge. They make a raid on Bolli in a dairy hut, where he fights a lone defense against fearful odds. Helgi Hardbeinsson deals Bolli a fatal wound and predicts that the child Gudrún is then carrying in her womb will be the death of him, Helgi. With this the main theme comes to a close — Gudrún's third dream and all of Gest's prophecies concerning the fates of Kjartan and Bolli have come to completion.

The postlude (chapters 57-end) is a working out of all the remaining prophecies — revenge for Bolli and Gudrún's fourth dream. Gudrún's friend and mentor, Snorri Godi, cunningly plans out both, securing for Gudrún the death of Helgi Hardbeinsson (just as Helgi had predicted) and a great chieftain as a fourth husband (just as her dream indicated). Gudrún lives out her life in remorse and mourning, confessing to her son Bolli Bollason which man she loved most: "To him I was worst whom I loved most." The saga has come full circle, the passions of hatred have been spent; the reader's expectations have all been fulfilled.

Unity of Composition, Technique, and Style

Prophecy and fulfillment as an enactment of destiny set the pattern for the structure of the narrative. Popular belief in portents, curses, dreams, visions of second sight and the like are all utilized as a convenient literary convention in which to couch the oracles of fate. Their presence is neither fanciful nor artificial, but part of real life. With a fine sensitivity for human nature, the author cloaks these sudden flashes of insight in the ambiguity and uncertainty that human beings are wont to ascribe to premonitions, and they are so subtly imbedded in the natural circumstances that they are even likely to be overlooked. Thus the characters are able to shrug them off as something inexplicable, and the reader is left in some apprehension and doubt whether it will actually come true, how it will happen, and when.

Fate never operates as a *deus ex machina*. Very deftly the author has amalgamated the natural and the supernatural causes. The characters follow the dictates of their own hearts and the demands of the moral law, neither flinching before what is ordained nor attempting to avert the inevitable. The involvements of the characters are always precisely what the plot demands, and the plot allows only those characteristics to predominate which further the action and suit the design. Plot and character are thus reflections of one another.

The structure of the plot rests on preparation and subsequent fulfillment, just as destiny is the coming to completion of what was present in embryo from the beginning. In the light of this, one can also better assess the function of the prelude. Every thread of the narrative is knotted and tied. The author never forgets, and if the reader does, he will be reminded. The little phrase occurring with such frequency in the saga: "You would not have brought this up, if you did not know where it was to land," admirably sums up the author's working method. He never "brings something up" without reason, and he always knows where it is leading, "where it will come down."

This structure is carried out in miniature in the subordinate episodes and scenes, each minor hunch ultimately finding, sometimes over great spans, its complementary statement of fulfillment. The phrases "if I don't miss my guess," "it will come as no surprise to me," and so forth reappear with such consistency that the reader may take them as a cue to heed well what is said, to look for a consequence later.

In addition to outright prophetic statements the author employs other devices to carry through the same formal concept of anticipation and completion. The characters are introduced by perfunctory adjectives; later in the action they act out in word and deed these traits assigned to them. The reader then knows beforehand what to expect of them. Since character and plot are so mutually dependent, the characters are apt to appear as types. Strikingly many are those who are "unfair" and "hard to deal with," or tagged as "a big man and strong," "a paragon among men (women)" (cf. below, p. xxxix). And not only are we prepared for the types of characters, but also for the characters themselves through their inconspicuous inclusion in genealogical listings long before they enter the stage of action. Snorri Godi, for instance, is mentioned in a genealogy as early as chapter 7 but does not take part in the story until chapter 36; Gudrún's family branch is included in chapter 2 and is not picked up again until chapter 32; and the list of such examples could be greatly enlarged. Thus it has not been found prudent to leave these seemingly superfluous genealogical listings out of the translation and relegate them to footnotes, as some translators have done.

Until now the genealogies have been the last stronghold of appeal in the argument for the chronicle nature of the sagas (the modicum of historicity left to them undisputedly); their integral function in enhancing the esthetic design has been overlooked. For the modern reader, less interested perhaps in genealogy and unacquainted with the characters from other sagas (the sagas are often complementary — the light focusing on certain characters in one saga, who then fade into background figures in another), genealogical charts have been inserted in this edition at those places where the reader is most likely to get lost in the maze, or where a refresher is needed to bring new characters into relationship with the family lineages already mentioned.

Another important means by which the author facilitates relating back and forth and carrying through the strands of narrative is through repetition in the lexical items. The author does not need to state explicitly, as he so often does, that a prophecy has now run its course, or that "now" it was the same "as before" — this he also does by re-using the linguistic pattern. Furthermore the same device is effectively employed to evoke comparisons between themes, scenes, and characters. Despite the wealth of episodes and characters, a basic structural pattern is thus brought into focus. Indeed, it is only by the linguistic components that many of the relationships and juxtapositions can be recognized. As a guide for the fuller enjoyment of the saga, I shall illustrate a few of them:

Vigdís rewards the slave Ásgaut with the money ill-gotten by her husband Thórd saying: "Now the money has fallen into better hands" (chapter 16). Subsequently Thórd turns over all his property to Hoskuld and Óláf to safeguard it from Vigdís who has divorced him and would like to get half his property in settlement. Thórd on this occasion says to Hoskuld: "...now the money has fallen into better hands" (*ibid.*). Repetition of the phrase evens out their play, tit for tat.

The Irish are intimidated by the appearance of Óláf's warlike vessel and "a murmur of discontent" runs through their group (chapter 21). Upon seeing the cavalry of the Irish king Mýrkjartan, "a murmur of discontent" over the odds passes through Óláf's ranks, thus neatly equalizing through the repeated phrase the two sides in their fear and strength.

Geirmund owned a trusty sword, which he always carried with him: "This sword he called Footbite, and he never let it very far out of his sight" (chapter 29). At the party at Hjardarholt, where Kjartan's sword is stolen, it is said: "Kjartan had not been carrying his sword Konungsnaut around with him while going about these duties, although he was rarely in the habit of letting it very far out of his sight" (chapter 46). The reader already knows the roles assigned to each of the swords, and the lexical repetition in describing them is no accident on the part of the author. It underscores their juxtaposition.

Throughout the saga the lexical repetitions are a guide to the structure of the saga and the intent of the author. They are not brought in arbitrarily, nor are they evidence of lack of imagination — a rote parroting of formulae. The number of parallels and pairs is astonishing, and they serve a deliberate function: Kjartan and Bolli

Thorleiksson are characterized in similar phrases, yet are also counter-parts; Kjartan has his match in Bolli Bollason; Gudrún hers in Thor-gerd, and her counterpart in Hrefna. These relationships are always indicated by parallel and contrasting phrases. Two brothers of opposite temperaments are a regular theme in the saga, and parallels of all sorts abound. These repeated themes with their similar phrases either may point up a fulfillment of the expected or may set up equalities of matching and counterbalancing.

Another type of repetition in the saga which exceeds twofold occurrence I call recurrence, for the phrases become stereotyped and formulaic, running on indefinitely. One might possibly see in them crystallizations of oral clichés that have now been used in the new medium. The whole technique of repetition as a literary device no doubt derives from similar techniques known to oral traditional poetry. The recurring phrases are particularly noticeable in the activities in the round of existence — birth and marriage proposals, careers abroad, and deathbed scenes. Again the reader is placed in a known and closed world, just as he was with the prophecies. There are no essential surprises. The element of chance is all but eliminated, just as destiny cancels chance. And this limited and foreknown world is reflected in the language of the saga — we know what to expect even as to the lexical choices.

Since the author has integrated the supernatural sphere (fate) with the moral realm (code of honor and revenge) — the one being the reflection of the other — the structural devices of repetition and recurrence symbolize the formal aspects of both. Repetition is a type of apparition of destiny, in that it underscores the fulfillment. On the other hand it balances the score, in a like-for-like compensating that mirrors the code of justice in its equal retaliation aspect. Recurrence enhances the sense of a predetermined and calculated world — life caught in its own mesh of formulae — inescapable, unalterable. On the other hand recurrence represents the run-on chain of endless revenge killings, the other aspect of the moral order.

The author also works with units of three, thereby reinforcing the tripartite division of the saga and the dominance of three main characters. There are, for example, three parties, each one patterned after the other; three goadings; three drownings, and three land sales, each with their reappearing motifs.

It would be tempting to multiply the examples of the author's technique, lest the subtleties be missed, for this overruling design permeates every level of the saga. But it would go beyond the purpose of this introduction to enumerate them further.[7] Suffice it to say that the reader's attention should be drawn to these repetitions and parallels, which I hope have survived in the translation.

If an analogy were to be given, I suppose the bargaining process itself, the evening of sides and meting out of justice would serve as the most apt image to express what the saga is about. There is a marked preference for weighing of evens and odds, of equalities and inequalities in every sort of dealing — be it comparison of men and their worth, wergild compensations, land sales, skirmishes, horse trades, or marriage contracts. The pulling back and forth, evening the trade, sizing up the odds, considering that a neighbor has "much land and little cattle," or "little land and much cattle" are all conspicuous elements throughout the saga.

The up-down, back-forth movement related to the weighing and balancing process sets up a counter-rhythm to the dramatic sweep of destiny that carries the action forward — it is a measured step and counterstep. The primacy of the natural sequence of prelude, central theme, and postlude (the chronological progression of "before," "now," and "after" — historical time) is thereby somewhat weakened — a good indication that the story moves in virtual time not practical time. But enough of the semblance of real time is retained in the succession of the generations to insure the likeness to historical account.

Something remains to be said of the over-all tone and style. Here again the author works with contrasts and alternations. There is a certain discrepancy between the restrained and precise form and the violence of the content — a fact which lends an ironic cast to the whole. This quality is especially conspicuous in the ambiguity in idioms, the tension between the apparent meaning and the significant meaning. Also part of the ironic tinge lies in the anonymity and impartiality of the author-creator who sees everything from above, something like fate operating from behind the scenes. To observe not so much *what* is being said, but *how* it is being said is one of the most interesting features in reading the saga.

The general splendor and formulaic superlative expressions also stand in contrast to the restrained presentation — hyperbole alternating with litotes. The background of ennobled reality heightens the tragic happenings. It is the most illustrious of the race that are doomed for a tragic end. Likewise there is a contrast between periods of relative calm and stormy violence. The saga rarely affords us descriptive passages, but the following reference to the weather sums up this type of alternation admirably: "The weather was squally, gusting to a sharp gale when the showers came on, but with scarcely any breeze between times" (chapter 18). Sunshine and gaiety almost always harbor a thundercloud that grows increasingly more menacing, turning the casual into the inevitable. We are plunged from hope to despair, from merriment to apprehension, where the first is almost the prerequisite for the second. The comic and tragic often stand side by side.

Although the central theme is basically tragic, the postlude ends on an upbeat. The genealogies continue, the life process begins anew, balance is restored. This is essentially the comic rhythm, and it is probably for this reason that some of the tragic impact is lost. Perhaps the formal structure is too mechanical, too pat, the detachment too great for us to become really involved with the characters. Be that as it may, the author has combined the comic and tragic elements to enhance his basic notion. Destiny and the moral code are brilliantly displayed in the precision of his form which reflects the rigidity and mechanical quality of this conception of life. Although its romantic theme sets it apart from most of the other sagas, and although Gudrún is one of the most well-drawn characters in saga literature, *Laxdoela* is not primarily a story of character development. It is more than a tragedy of human beings; it is the tragedy of a way of life.

Out of his "givens" and within the framework of his all-pervasive design, the author has created a vivid illusion of historical actuality. With a sureness of touch he has woven his pattern, arranging his material from the past and present. The historical material, the occasional but deliberate appeal to authority (by using Ari Thorgilsson's name [the founder of Icelandic historical discipline] and including poems), the lavish use of proper names and proper settings all contribute to the illusion of actuality. We are in a real place, in a real time, and with real persons. It is the arrangement of these factors in a pattern that lifts the work outside of history and gives it symbolic significance beyond its discursive content. The author's awareness of the irretractable demands of wounded honor, of the lust for revenge and the greed for power, his perception of an unavoidable destiny, his dark consciousness of the inescapable entanglements of life "then" and "now" made it possible for him to conceive a work that embraces the spirit of the Commonwealth as well as the spirit of the Sturlunga Age. It can delight the twentieth-century reader with its freshness and unstilted idiom, its sensitivity to human nature, its cool detachment, and tautness of structure.

This Translation

Three renderings of the saga into English have preceded this one: by Muriel A. C. Press (1899), by Robert Proctor (1905), and by Thorstein Veblen (1925). They paved the way, smoothing many a stone from the path as well as showing up the pitfalls. All three of them contained some serious drawbacks, ranging from gross inaccuracies to too archaic and mannered a style. Just like fashions, modes of translation change and have a history of their own. Thus in many respects a new translation seemed warranted. The tendency today departs from the former practices of employing as many esoteric cognates and loan translations as the English could bear. Mrs. Press makes attempts in this direction, and Proctor's work is a veritable curiosity. Veblen's fault lies mainly in his inaccuracies and the poor edition of 1826 which he used as a basis for his translation.

In this translation I proceeded on the theory that the natural idiom and tone of the sagas should be represented by a cast of language that is as palatable as everyday speech and as fresh as it was seven hundred years ago. The saga text combines an artistic semblance of the spoken word with meticulous literary composition. This fact imparts a dignity to the informal language with its colloquialisms and clichés that characterizes the over-all linguistic fabric.

A translator is always obliged to gauge the niceties of flavor, the pejorative overtones, the epigrammatic terseness, proverbialisms, and subtleties of the text — a flash of irony here, a shade of meaning there. Thus literalness sometimes must be sacrificed to interpretative renderings that strike the spirit rather than the letter. The ambiguities and ironic tinge of the original have posed the greatest difficulties. The lexical repetitions and the precision of arrangement can also not be lost without losing the import of the whole. It has been my aim to preserve these characteristics within the limits of possibility, and it is hoped that they will shine through in the translation.

It should be noted that proverbial sayings often have an archaic ring, though they continue to be used in fossilized form in everyday speech. Similarly, some of the phrases in the saga seem to be time-worn and crystallized; thus "he was a big man and strong," or "she (he) was a paragon among women (men)" appear in the text as tags of common stock and trade, conventionalized and formulaic.

A word remains to be said about the poems in the saga, although there are but five short ones. Hólmgongu-Bersi's ditty (chapter 28) and Thorgils' verse after the raid (chapter 65) are in end rhyme; Aud's two lines of verse (chapter 25), the warning of Thorgils' *fylgja,* and the riddle spoken by the cloak (chapter 67) are alliterative verse. These qualities, as well as the rhythm of the poems, I have tried to imitate in the translations.

One of the most obvious features of the Icelandic sagas is the abundance of proper names. Since there is no one generally accepted standard in the treatment of Icelandic names in translation, I have tried to set up some working principles. In general the underlying aim has been to retain the appearance of the word so that reference to the original text and to maps may be facilitated.

The orthography has been adapted to the English alphabet as follows: (1) the acute accent has been retained; (2) the Icelandic letters ǫ and ø have been transliterated as *o*; (3) the two digraphs *oe* and *ae* have been written apart; (4) the voiceless and voiced spirants þ and ð have been replaced by *th* and *d* respectively; (5) the final nominative case ending *-r* has been dropped after consonants, retained after vowels; (6) the double final consonants have been simplified when a result of assimilation with the case ending, retained when part of the stem of the word.

The accent mark indicates length of vowel, not stress. The Old

Icelandic vowels have the continental values: *á* is pronounced like the *a* in English *father* (in modern Icelandic this long *á* has been diphthongized to *[au]* as in English *cow*). Thus the name Án, for instance, may be pronounced with long vowel or the diphthong. The Old Icelandic long *ó* has also been diphthongized and may be pronounced like the *o* in English *note*. Long *ú* is as *oo* in English *school;* long *í* and *ý* as *ee* in English *green*. The modern Icelandic grammatical forms and syntax have remained so close to the language of the thirteenth century that the sagas can be read in Iceland today with ease by the layman. It may be of interest to the reader that the sagas are read aloud as serial stories on the radio, where the modern pronunciation is of course used.

Each of the classes of proper names presented special problems. Some of the practices that might cause difficulty for the English reader should be briefly noted here. *Patronymics* in *-son* and *-dóttir* (English equivalents — "son" and "daughter") are not surnames and have literal meaning: Óláf Hoskuldsson is the equivalent of Óláf, the son of Hoskuld. The Icelandic forms have been retained in the translation as well as the equivalent lengthened forms. The reader should note that while many of the patronymic compounds have an *s*-genitive familiar to English, some names have other possessive forms and therefore exhibit a vowel change within the stem of the name: thus Jórunn *Bjarnar*dóttir is the same as Jórunn, the daughter of *Bjorn*; and Thorgils *Hollu*son is the son of *Halla*. It is hoped that the reader will soon adjust to these changes after some familiarizing with the text and by exercising a spark of imagination.

Bynames are generally translated or given English equivalents in parentheses, since they add much to the characterization. Obscure, ludicrous, or offensive ones are explained in footnotes.

Place names in *-dal* (English "dale"), *-stadir* (English "-stead"), and *-fjord* (English "fjord") should pose no difficulties for the reader. Tautological renderings of names in *-á* (English "river"), *-eyjar* (English "islands"), and *-heidi* (English "heath") have been avoided. With river names (as well as with fjord names when the waterway itself is meant) the definite article has been used: thus "the Laxá," much as we say "the Missouri," "the Thames." Names in *-á* in the text should thus be recognized as river names. Circumlocutions such as "those islands called the Brenneyjar," or "the moorlands of the Bláskóga-heidi" are used in the other instances.

Inhabitant names have been so rendered as to facilitate for the English reader the association of the people with their proper geographic district or farm. The _Eyfirðingar_ has been translated "the Eyfirthers," that is to say the inhabitants of the Eyjafjord. The _Hjarðhyltingar_ becomes in translation the "Hjardholters," which should be readily associated with the farm Hjardarholt.

Some inconsistencies naturally arise; where rigid adherence to a system became absurd, inconsistency proved preferable.

The translation is based on the edition of Einar Ó. Sveinsson, Vol. V of _Íslenzk fornrit_ (Reykjavík, 1934), which is edited from the _Möðruvallabók_. Any reading incorporated or substituted is so indicated in a footnote; this has occurred in but three or four instances. In general, footnotes elucidate difficult or obscure names, discuss customs or practices not readily comprehensible from the context, or give historical facts relevant to the text. Genealogical charts have been included as well as some maps. The chapter headings are my innovation, and attempt to give hints and parallels in accordance with the author's method and intention.

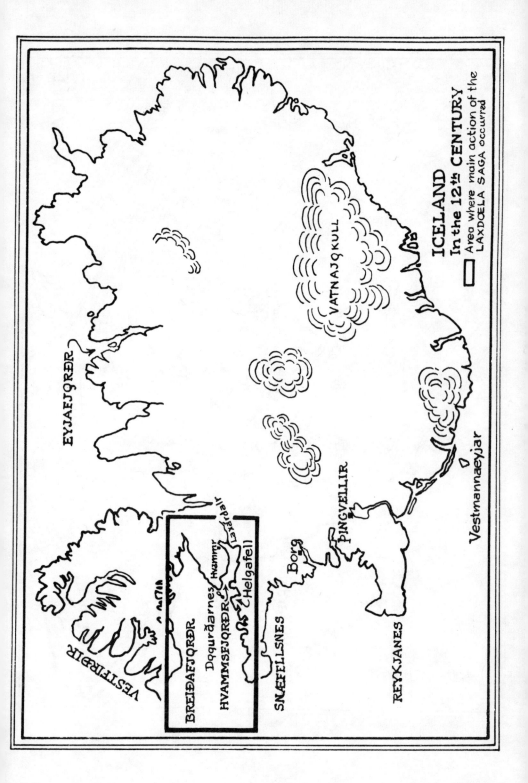

ICELAND
In the 12ᵗʰ CENTURY

▢ Area where main action of the
LAXDŒLA SAGA occurred

VATNAJÖKULL

EYJAFJÖRÐR

VESTFIRÐIR

BREIÐAFJÖRÐR
Dǫgurðarnes Hvammr
HVAMMSFJÖRÐR
Helgafell
Laxárdalr

SNÆFELLSNES

Borg

ÞINGVELLIR

REYKJANES

Vestmannaeyjar

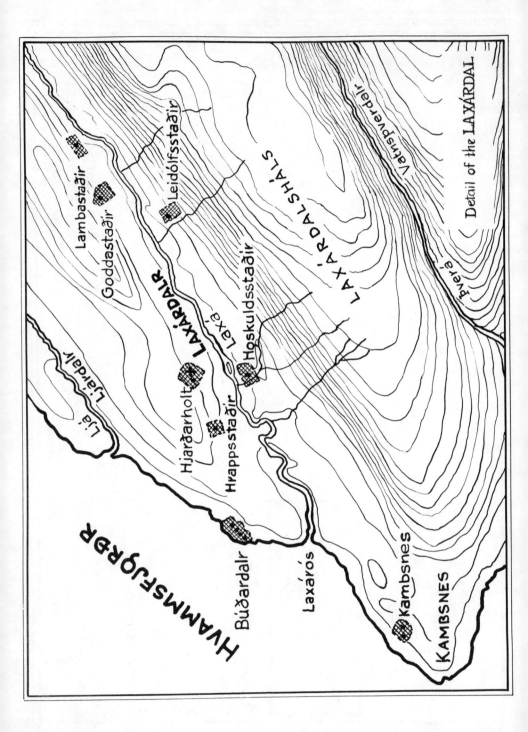

Detail of the LAXÁRDAL

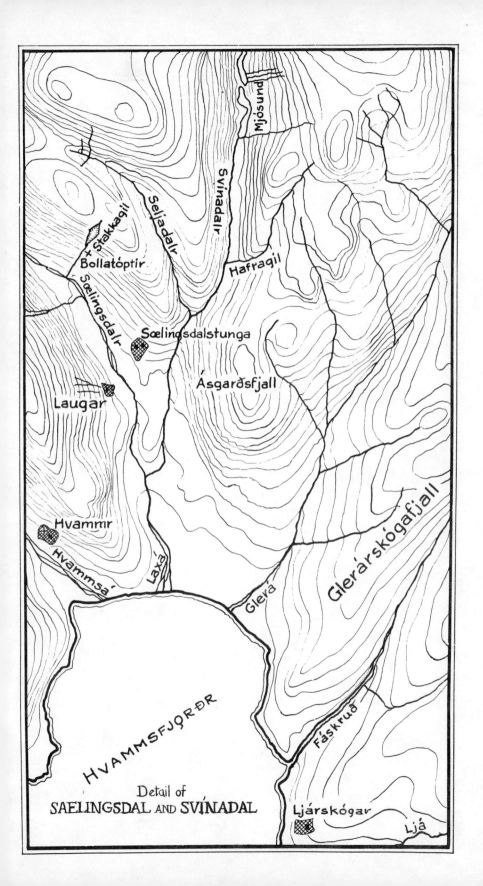

Detail of
SAELINGSDAL AND SVÍNADAL

THE
LAXDOELA SAGA

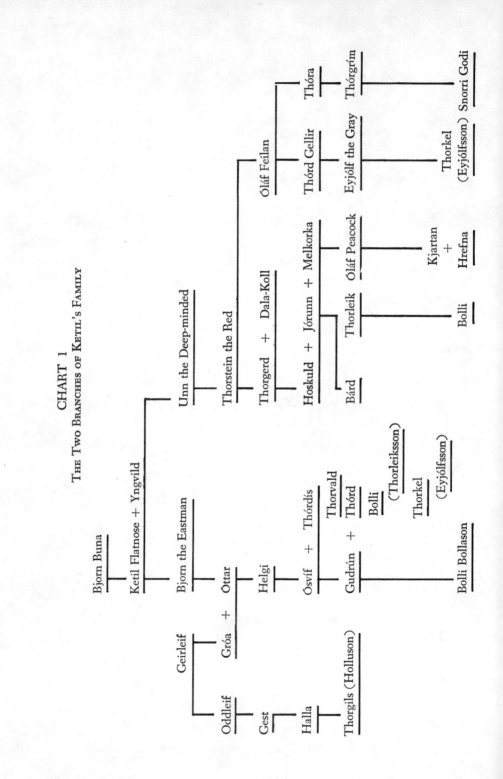

CHART 1
THE TWO BRANCHES OF KETIL'S FAMILY

1

Ketil Flatnose and His Kin

THERE was a man named Ketil Flatnose, the son of Bjorn Buna (Clumsy Foot). He was a powerful local ruler[1] in Norway and high-born. He lived in Romsdal in the Romsdal District, which lies between Sunnmoere and Nordmoere. Ketil Flatnose was married to Yngvild, daughter of Ketil Wether, a fine and splendid man. They had five children. One son was called Bjorn the Eastman, another Helgi Bjólan.[2] Thórunn Hyrna,[3] one of Ketil's daughters, was married to Helgi the Lean. He was the son of Eyvind the Eastman and Rafarta, the daughter of the Irish king Kjarval. Unn the Deep-minded was a second daughter of Ketil; she was the wife of Óláf the White,[4] the son of Ingjald, who was the son of Fródi the Brave whom the Svertlings[5] slew. Jórunn Manvitsbrekka[6] was a third daughter of Ketil. She was the mother of Ketil the Lucky Fisherman, who took a land claim at Kirkjubaer.[7] His son was Ásbjorn, who was the father of Surt, who was the father of Sighvat the Lawspeaker.

2

Troubles Ahead

IN THE latter days of Ketil, King Harald Fairhair rose to such great power that no local king nor any other prominent man could prosper in the land, since King Harald alone had authority over all ranks and titles. Now when it came to Ketil's knowledge that King Harald had the same fate in mind for him as for other men of high rank — namely of seeing his kinsmen unatoned and himself made into tenant farmer to boot — he summoned his kinsmen for a parley: "It is well known to you what dealings have passed between me and King Harald," he said, "so there's no need to go into that. It is much more urgent for us to discuss the troubles which we now have to face. I have sure knowledge of King Harald's hostility toward us, so we certainly can't expect anything good from that quarter. As I see it, we have two choices — to flee the country or be slain, each under his own roof. I myself would rather end my days as my forefathers have, but I don't want to lead you into such great trials on my persuasion, for I well know the attitude of my kinsmen and friends — you will want to stick together, even if following me would mean putting your mettle to somewhat of a test."

Ketil's son Bjorn was quick to answer: "I'll make my wish known. I want to follow the example of noble men and flee this land. I do not see what would be gained by waiting at home for King Harald's thralls to drive us from our holdings or to kill us outright." For this there was good applause, and they all thought he had spoken like a man. It was decided that they would leave the country, since Ketil's sons were so eager to do so and no one spoke up against it. Bjorn and Helgi wanted to go to Iceland, for they apparently had heard many favorable things from there. They said opportunities to get land there were good, and one did not have to pay for it.[1] There was frequent stranding of whales and good salmon fishing, they said; and the fishing grounds were open all year round. Ketil answered: "To those fishing grounds I shall never come in my old age." Ketil then said he was more of a mind to go west across the sea.[2] Livelihood there was considered good, he declared, and the lands round about were known to him, for in his youth[3] he had harried there far and wide.

3

Westward Across the Sea

AFTER this Ketil had a splendid feast; it was then he married off his daughter Thórunn Hyrna to Helgi the Lean, as was said before. This done, Ketil got ready for his journey abroad and set out westward across the sea. His daughter Unn went with him and many of his other kinsmen.

Ketil's sons together with Helgi the Lean, their brother-in-law, also set sail that summer for Iceland. Bjorn Ketilsson steered his ship round to the west and up into the Breidafjord, sailing close along the southern side to a point where the fjord cut into the land. A high mountain stood on the headland inside the fjord, and an island lay a short distance offshore. Bjorn said they would make a stop for a while. He went ashore with some men and strolled along the sea. There was a narrow strip of land between the mountain and the shore, and Bjorn thought it a good place to live. There he found the pillars of his high-seat washed ashore in the bay, and it seemed to them all that this spot was indeed meant to be their dwelling place.[1] Thereupon Bjorn laid claim to all the land between the Stafá[2] and the Hraunsfjord. The place where he lived was called Bjarnarhofn, and it has had that name ever since. He was called Bjorn the Eastman. His wife was Gjaflaug, who was the daughter of Kjallak the Old. Their sons were Óttar and Kjallak. Kjallak had a son called Thorgrím, who was the father of Víga-Styr (Slayer-Styr) and Vermund; and he had a daughter called Helga. She was married to Vestar from Eyr, the son of Thórólf the Braggart, who was the first settler at Eyr. Their son was Thorlák, the father of Steinthór from Eyr.

Helgi Bjólan came with his ship to the south part of Iceland and claimed all the land on Kjalarnes between the Kollafjord and the Hvalfjord. He lived at Esjuberg until old age. Helgi the Lean came with his ship to the north part of Iceland and took up all the land around the Eyjafjord between Siglunes and Reynisnes and dwelt at Kristnes. From Helgi and Thórunn have descended the Eyfirth kin.

CHART 2

KETIL'S CHILDREN AND THEIR KIN

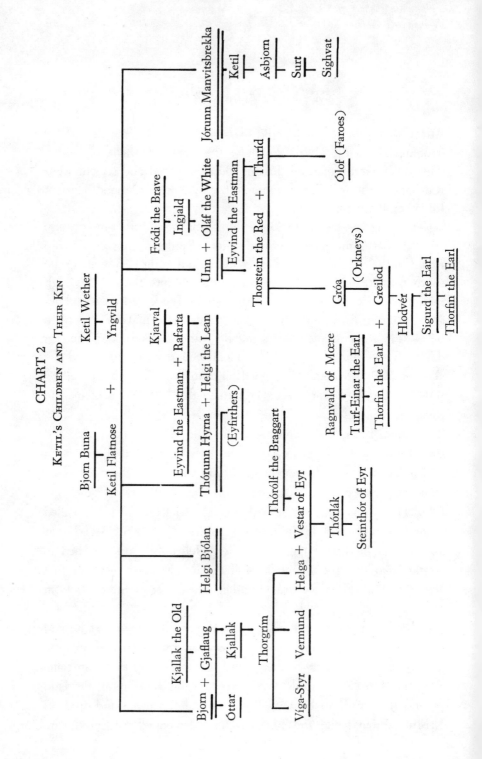

4

Ketil's Kin in Scotland

KETIL Flatnose came with his ship to Scotland and was well received there by noble men, for he himself was a famous man and high-born. They offered him whatever station in life he chose to have. Ketil and some of his kinsmen settled down there — all except Thorstein, the son of his daughter Unn. Thorstein set out at once on freebooting raids and harried far and wide around Scotland, always coming out the victor. Later he reached a settlement with the Scots, taking for himself half of Scotland, over which he made himself king. He was married to Thuríd, the daughter of Eyvind and sister of Helgi the Lean. The truce was short-lived, for the Scots soon broke their oath and betrayed Thorstein. Ari Thorgilsson the Learned reports that Thorstein met his end at Caithness.[1]

Unn the Deep-minded was at Caithness when her son Thorstein fell. With the news of his killing, Unn felt she did not have much chance of recovering her position there, now that her father too was dead. So she secretly had a ship built in the woods, and when it was ready, she fitted it out with a wealth of goods, and all her kinsmen who were still alive went with her. People say the likes can scarcely be found of any one woman getting out of such straits with as much wealth and goods and with such a large company. From this it can be seen what a paragon among women Unn was.

Unn also had with her many men who were of much account and high-born. There was a man by the name of Koll; he was by far the most illustrious in Unn's company, mostly because of his lineage, for he bore the title of *hersir*.[2] There was also a man by the name of Hord in Unn's following. He too was of high birth and counted for much. When everything was ready, Unn sailed to the Orkneys, where she stayed for some time. There she married off Gróa, Thorstein the Red's daughter. Gróa was the mother of Greilod, who was married to Thorfin the Earl, who was the son of Turf-Einar the Earl,[3] who was the son of Ragnvald, Earl of Moere. Their son was Hlodvér, who was the father of Sigurd the Earl, who was the father

of Thorfin the Earl. From them have descended all the earls of
Orkney.

Unn then sailed to the Faroe Islands, where she also stayed for
some time and there married off Thorstein's second daughter. Her
name was Ólof and from her has descended the most renowned family
in the land, the Gotuskeggjar.[4]

5

Unn the Deep-minded and Her High-mindedness

Now Unn made ready to leave the Faroe Islands and announced to
her crew that she intended to sail for Iceland. She had with her
Óláf Feilan,[1] Thorstein the Red's son, and those of his sisters who
were not yet married. She put out to sea and had a good voyage and
came with her ship to the southern side of Iceland at Vikrarskeid.[2]
There they were shipwrecked, but all the men and goods were saved.

Thereafter Unn went in a party of twenty to pay a visit to her
brother Helgi. Helgi went out to meet her and invited her to stay
with a party of ten in all. She answered him back sharply, said she
had not known he was such a petty person, and with that turned
about and left. Now she made up her mind to visit her brother Bjorn
in Breidafjord. When he heard about her coming, he went out to meet
her with a large following and welcomed her and invited her to stay
with her whole party, for he well knew his sister's bent. She was
most pleased and thanked him for his generosity. She stayed there
through the winter and was entertained liberally, for there was plenty
of provisions and nothing was stinted.

In the spring she sailed across the Breidafjord and lay in at a headland where they ate their morning meal. That place has been called
Dogurdarnes (Daymeal Ness)[3] ever since. The Medalfellsstrond[4]
extends from there. Next Unn sailed in along the Hvammsfjord and
came to another headland where she made a short stay. There Unn
lost her comb, so ever since this headland has been called Kambsnes
(Comb's Ness). She went all around the Breidafjord Dales, claiming
land thereabouts, as far and wide as she pleased.

Finally Unn sailed her ship up the fjord to its very head. There the pillars of her high-seat had drifted ashore; so now it seemed plain to her where she was to take up her abode. She had a farmstead built and called it Hvamm — a name it has had ever since — and there it was that she lived.

The same spring that Unn set up her household at Hvamm, Koll was wedded to Thorgerd, Thorstein the Red's daughter. Unn stood the cost of that wedding feast and let Thorgerd have the whole Laxárdal as a dowry. There, to the south of the Laxá, she and Koll set up a homestead. Koll was a man who commanded great personal respect. Their son was Hoskuld.

6

Unn's Generosity

THEREAFTER Unn portioned out sectors of her land claim to one and another of her men. To Hord she gave Hordadal,[1] all the way up to the Skrámuhlaupsá. He dwelt at Hordabólstad and was a man of great note and fortunate in his children. His son was Ásbjörn the Wealthy who lived at Ásbjarnarstadir in Ornólfsdal. His wife was Thorbjorg, the daughter of Midfjardar-Skeggi (Skeggi of Midfjord). Their daughter was Ingibjorg, whom Illugi the Black had for a wife. Their sons were Hermund and Gunnlaug Ormstunga.[2] This family line is known as the Gilsbekking kin.[3]

One day Unn said to her bondmen: "The time has now come for you to be repaid for your toil and willing service. It is known to you all that I have given freedom to a certain man by the name of Erp, the son of Meldun the Earl. It was far from my will that such a high-born man be called a bondman." Thereupon Unn gave him all the Saudafell lands between the Tunguá and the Midá. His children were Orm and Ásgeir, Gunnbjorn and Halldís, whom Dala-Álf[4] had as a wife. To Sokkólf Unn gave Sokkólfsdal, and he dwelt there until old age. Hundi was the name of another freedman of Unn's. He was a Scotsman by birth; to him she gave Hundadal. Vífil was the name of a fourth bondman of Unn's; to him she gave Vífilsdal.

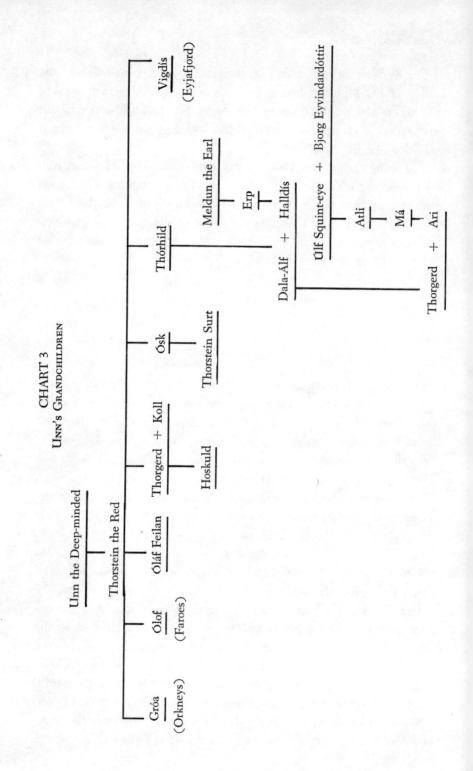

CHART 3
UNN'S GRANDCHILDREN

Thorstein the Red's fourth daughter was called Ósk. She was the mother of Thorstein Surt the Wise, who introduced the summer eke.[5] Thórhild was Thorstein's fifth daughter. She was the mother of Álf of the Dales; many a man can trace his lineage back to him. His daughter was Thorgerd, who was the wife of Ari, who was the son of Má from Reykjanes, who was the son of Atli, who was the son of Úlf Squint-eye and his wife Bjorg Eyvindardóttir, who was the sister of Helgi the Lean. From Thorgerd and Ari have descended the Reykjanes kin. Vigdís was the name of Thorstein the Red's sixth daughter. From her have descended the Hofdi kin[6] in Eyjafjord.

CHART 4

EYVIND THE EASTMAN'S CONNECTION WITH KETIL AND UNN

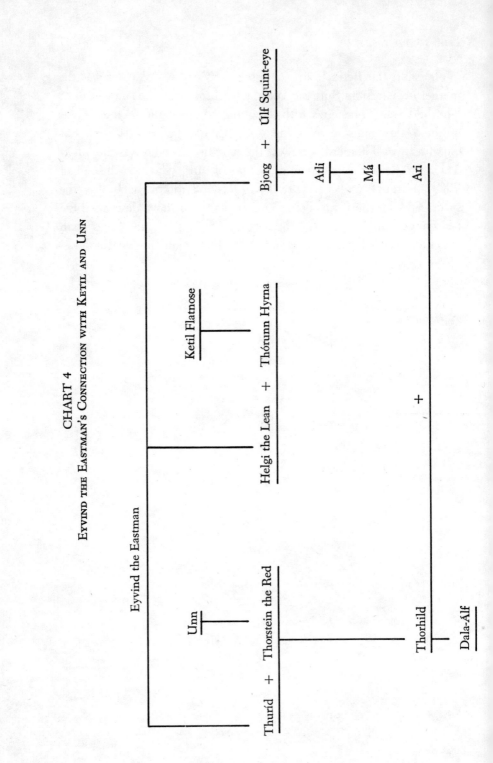

Eyvind the Eastman

Thuríd + Thorstein the Red

Unn

Helgi the Lean + Thórunn Hyrna

Ketil Flatnose

Bjorg + Úlf Squint-eye

Atli

Má

Ari

Thorhild

Dala-Álf

7

Unn's Last Days

ÓLÁF Feilan was the youngest of Thorstein's children. He was a big man and strong, good-looking and of many accomplishments. Unn esteemed him above all others and let it be known to her kinsmen that she intended all her property at Hvamm to go to Óláf after her day. Unn was now growing very weary with old age. She called Óláf to her and said: "It has occurred to me, kinsman, that you ought to settle down and get married." Óláf took this in good part and said he would rely on her judgment. Unn said: "I have rather thought your wedding feast might come at the end of this summer, for that is the easiest time to get provisions; and if I don't miss my guess, a great number of our friends will be coming here, for I expect to prepare this feast as my last one." Óláf answered: "What you say is all very well, but I shall see to it that I get the kind of wife who will rob you of neither your wealth nor your authority."

That same fall Óláf Feilan took Álfdís as his wife, and the wedding feast was at Hvamm. Unn was put to great expense for this feast, for she had invited people of high estate from far and wide and out of other districts. She asked her brothers Bjorn and Helgi Bjólan, and they came with many people. Her son-in-law Koll from the Dales and Hord from Hordadal also came, as well as many other men of high rank. There was a large gathering of guests present, although not anywhere near as many came as Unn had invited, for the Eyfirthers had too long a way to come.

By this time old age was coming hard upon Unn, so much so that she did not rise before midday and lay down early to sleep. She never permitted anyone to seek counsel of her between the time she went to bed in the evening and when she was up and dressed in the morning. She answered back sharply if anyone so much as asked about her health.

On the day of the wedding, Unn slept longer than was her wont, but was up and about all the same when the wedding guests arrived. She went out to meet them and with all due honor bade her kinsmen and friends welcome. She said they had shown her much considera-

tion by coming such a long way. "It is Bjorn and Helgi I am especially thinking of in this regard, but I want to thank all of you for coming
here," she said. Then Unn walked into the hall, and a large company
with her. And after the hall was filled and the guests seated, everyone
marveled at how magnificent a feast it was. Then Unn spoke: "I call
you to witness, Bjorn, my brother, and Helgi, as well as you other
kinsmen and friends — this homestead, with such stock and stores as
you can now see, I put into the hands of my kinsman Óláf; it is for
him to have and to hold." After that Unn rose from her seat and said
that she was going to retire to the chamber where she was used to
sleeping. She begged them each and all to find whatever amusement
suited them best and asked that ale be served all around. People say
Unn was both tall and sturdy; and as she now walked with firm step
along the hall, people could not help but remark what a stately
woman she was. The men drank throughout the evening until they
thought it time for bed.

The following day Óláf Feilan went to the sleeping chamber of
Unn, his kinswoman; and when he came into her room, there she
was, propped up against her pillow. Unn was dead. Óláf went back
to the hall and told these tidings. Everyone thought it remarkable
how Unn had kept her dignity up to the day of her death. Now
there was drinking to both things — Óláf's wedding and Unn's funeral
feast. On the last day of the feast, Unn was carried to the burial
mound prepared for her. She was laid in a ship in the mound, and
much wealth was laid there with her. Afterwards the mound was
covered over.

With the consent of those kinsmen present at the feast, Óláf Feilan
took over the farmstead at Hvamm with the disposition of all its
wealth and property. When the feast was over and the guests were
departing, Óláf presented generous gifts to the most prominent of
them. Óláf became a man of power and was a great chieftain. He
lived at Hvamm until old age. Óláf and Álfdís had these children:
there was Thórd Gellir (the Yeller) who was married to Hródný, the
daughter of Skeggi of Midfjord; their sons were Eyjólf the Gray,
Thórarin Fylsenni (Foal's Forehead) and Thorkel Kuggi.[1] And then
Óláf and Álfdís had a daughter Thóra, who was married to Thorstein
Thorskabít,[2] the son of Thórólf of Moster.[3] Their sons were Bork the

Stout and Thorgrím, who was the father of Snorri Godi.[4] Helga was the name of Óláf's second daughter and she was married to Gunnar Elífarson. Their daughter was Jófríd, who was first married to Thórodd, Tungu-Odd's son,[5] and later to Thorstein Egilsson. Gunnar and Helga had another daughter named Thórunn. She was the wife of Herstein, the son of Thorkel, who was the son of Sleepy-Ketil. A third daughter of Óláf's was called Thórdís; she was the wife of Thórarin the Lawspeaker, the brother of Ragi.

While Óláf was living at Hvamm, his brother-in-law Dala-Koll took sick and died. Koll's son Hoskuld was just a young lad when his father died, but was more mature of mind than the number of his years told. He was both handsome and capable. Hoskuld took over his father's whole estate; and the farm on which Koll had lived was called Hoskuldsstadir after him — a name which it has had ever since. Hoskuld came to be very popular, for he found many supporters among his kinsmen and from the friends his father Koll had made.

Thorgerd Thorsteinsdóttir, mother of Hoskuld, was still young and a very beautiful woman. After Koll's death, she was not very happy in Iceland and told her son Hoskuld that she wanted to go abroad with such wealth as fell to her share. Hoskuld said it was a shame for them to have to part, but that he would no more oppose her wishes in this than in anything else. Then Hoskuld bought his mother half interest in a ship drawn ashore at Dogurdarnes. Thorgerd set out for the ship, taking much wealth with her. Thereafter she put out to sea and her ship had a good voyage and made Norway. Thorgerd had a great number of relatives there and many noble kinsmen. They gave her a good welcome and offered her anything and everything she would accept from them. Thorgerd took this in good part, saying she had in mind to settle down in Norway.

Thorgerd was not a widow long before a man came to ask for her hand. His name was Herjólf; he was of the landed aristocracy,[6] wealthy and highly esteemed. Herjólf was a big man and strong; he was not handsome, but fine and manly looking, one of the best of fighters and very skilled in arms. When this marriage proposal came up for settlement, it was Thorgerd's privilege to give her own answer, for she was a widow. So, with the assent of her kinsmen she accepted this proposal and married Herjólf and went to his homestead to live, and they grew to love one another dearly. Thorgerd proved to be a most exceptional and capable woman, and Herjólf's circumstances were thought to be all the better and even worthier of esteem than before, now that he had got such a wife as Thorgerd.

CHART 5

THORSTEIN THE RED'S SON ÓLÁF FEILAN AND HIS KIN

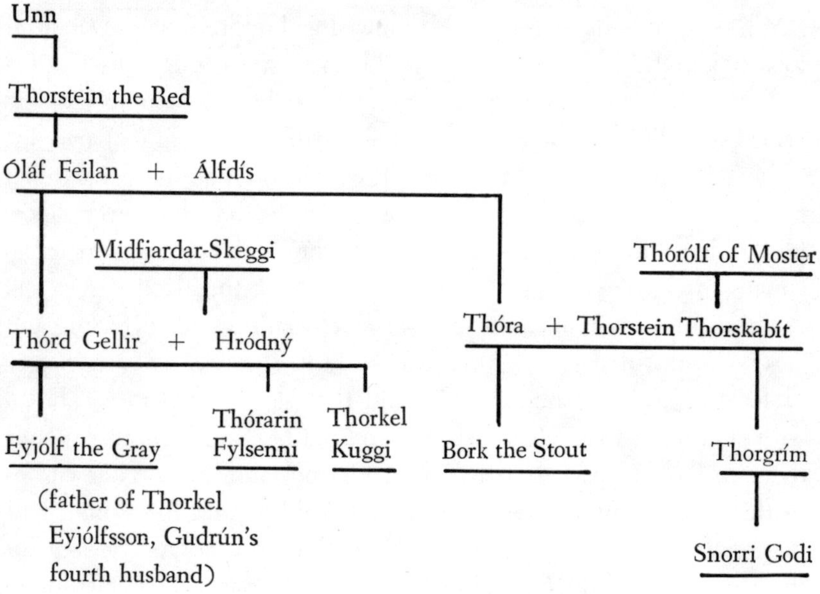

Unn
|
Thorstein the Red
|
Óláf Feilan + Álfdís

Midfjardar-Skeggi

Thórólf of Moster

Thórd Gellir + Hródný   Thóra + Thorstein Thorskabít

Thórarin   Thorkel
Fylsenni   Kuggi

Eyjólf the Gray   Bork the Stout   Thorgrím

(father of Thorkel
Eyjólfsson, Gudrún's
fourth husband)

Snorri Godi

8

The Undivided Inheritance

HERJÓLF and Thorgerd had not been married long before a son was born to them. The boy was sprinkled with water[1] and given a name; he was called Hrút. He very early grew to be big and strong. He had a better build than most — tall, broad-shouldered, slim-waisted, with well-knit arms and legs. He was the handsomest of men, just as his mother's father Thorstein had been or Ketil Flatnose. All in all he was most accomplished.

Herjólf took sick and died. To many that seemed a great loss.

Thereafter Thorgerd longed to go back to Iceland to visit her son
Hoskuld, for she loved him above all else. Hrút was left behind in
good hands with his kinsmen. Thorgerd set out for Iceland, and once
there, went to visit her son Hoskuld in Laxárdal. He received his
mother with due respect. She had brought a wealth of goods along
and stayed with Hoskuld until the day of her death; that took place
only a few years after her return. She was laid in a burial mound.
Hoskuld took over all her property, and half of it was his brother
Hrút's.

CHART 6
THORSTEIN THE RED'S DAUGHTER THORGERD AND HER KIN

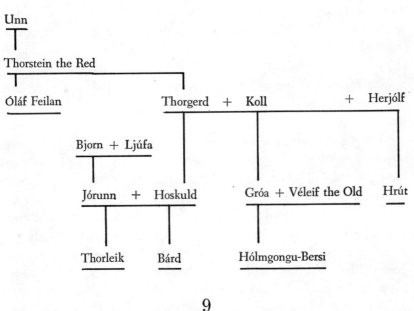

9

Hoskuld and His Kin

AT THIS time Hákon, Adalstein's foster son,[1] was king of Norway.
Hoskuld was in the king's guard and always spent his winters either
with the king or on his own farm at home. He was a renowned man
both in Norway and in Iceland. There was a man named Bjorn who
lived at Bjarnarfjord, where he had taken a land claim; the fjord is

named after him. This fjord cuts into the land north of the
Steingrímsfjord, and there is a neck of land extending out between
the two fjords. Bjorn was a high-born man and wealthy; his wife's
name was Ljúfa. Their daughter was Jórunn.[2] She was a beautiful
woman, very prideful and vain, and exceptionally sharp-witted. At
that time she was considered the best match in all the Westfjords.
Hoskuld had heard much about this woman and also that Bjorn was
the most highly regarded farmer in the whole region of the Strands.[3]

Hoskuld rode from home together with nine other men to visit
Bjorn in Bjarnarfjord. He was well received there, for Bjorn had
heard good reports of him. Hoskuld presently broached his proposal.
Bjorn gave good answer, saying he doubted whether his daughter
could be better married, but that he would nevertheless leave the
decision up to her. When the matter was set before Jórunn, she gave
this reply: "From all we have heard about you, Hoskuld, we should
like to give a favorable answer. We have reason to think that the
woman married to you will be well provided for. However my father
is to have the most to say in this, for I will agree to whatever he
wishes."

Be that as it may, the long and short of it was that Jórunn was
betrothed to Hoskuld with a large dowry. The wedding was to be at
Hoskuldsstadir. This settled and done, Hoskuld rode back to his own
farm and stayed at home until time for the wedding. Bjorn came to
the feast from the north with a handsome company. Hoskuld had
many guests there to greet them, both friends and kinsmen; and the
wedding was an exceptionally fine one. When it was over, everyone
departed for home in good friendship and with befitting gifts. Jórunn
Bjarnardóttir stayed behind at Hoskuldsstadir and took over the management of the household with Hoskuld. It was soon apparent from
all her ways that she would be wise and capable in all that she did,
though always rather proud-minded. It went well with their married
life, even if there was usually not much love lost between them.

Hoskuld now became a great chieftain. He had power and influence, was eager to get ahead, and did not lack for means. In no wise
was he deemed a man of lesser account than his father Koll had been.
Hoskuld and Jórunn had not been married long before children were
born to them. Their eldest son was named Thorleik; another son was

called Bárd. They had a daughter named Hallgerd, who later was nicknamed Long Breeches. Another daughter of theirs was called Thuríd. All Hoskuld's children showed promise.

Thorleik was a big man and strong and very handsome, but close-mouthed and rather unfriendly. From his disposition most people thought he would turn out to be unreasonable and hard to deal with. Hoskuld often remarked that Thorleik would likely take after the side of the family up at the Strands, his mother's kin. Hoskuld's son Bárd was also an exceptionally fine-looking young man, strong in body and mind. From his manner it looked as though he would favor his father's kinsmen. He was an easy, good-natured person and made many friends as he grew up. Of all his children Hoskuld loved Bárd the most. Hoskuld's house now stood in full flower and he enjoyed the highest esteem. About this time Hoskuld married off his sister Gróa to Véleif the Old. Their son was Hólmgongu-Bersi.[4]

10

Neighbor Troubles

THERE was a man called Hrapp who lived in Laxárdal on the north side of the river opposite Hoskuldsstadir. His farm was called Hrappsstadir — a name it has had ever since. It is now deserted there. Hrapp was the son of Sumarlidi and was called Víga-Hrapp.[1] He was Scottish on his father's side; his mother's kin were all in the Hebrides and that was where he was born. He was a big man and strong and never wanted to be worsted, even if the odds were considerably against him. And since he was so unreasonable and hard to deal with, as we just said, and was not willing to make amends for his misdeeds, he had fled westward across the sea to Iceland and had bought himself the land he was living on. His wife's name was Vigdís, Hallstein's daughter. Their son was called Sumarlidi. Vigdís' brother was Thorstein Surt, whom we have mentioned before; he was living at that time at Thórsnes.[2] There Sumarlidi was being fostered and he was a most promising lad. Thorstein had been married, but his wife was now dead. He had two daughters; one was called Gudríd and the other

Ósk. Gudríd was married to Thorkel Trefil,[3] who lived at Svignaskard. He was a great chieftain and a wise man; he was the son of Red-Bjorn. Thorstein's daughter Ósk was given in marriage to a Breidfirther by the name of Thórarin, a stalwart fellow and popular. He lived with his father-in-law Thorstein, who was now advanced in years and stood very much in need of his help.

Hrapp was not liked by most people. He was contrary and quarrel-some with his neighbors and hinted to them every now and then that he could make it mighty uncomfortable for them as neighbors if they held any man better than him. So all the farmers got together and were of one mind — to go to Hoskuld and tell him their grievances. Hoskuld told them to let him know if Hrapp ever gave them any trouble — "For he is not going to rob *me* of either life or property."

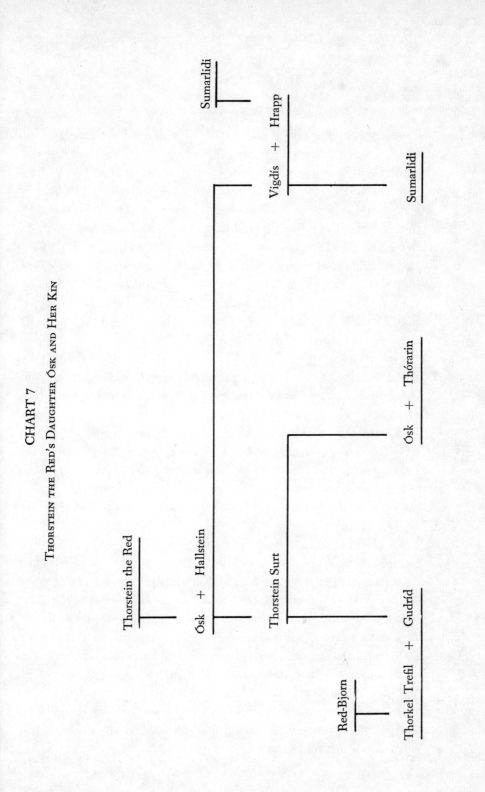

CHART 7

THORSTEIN THE RED'S DAUGHTER ÓSK AND HER KIN

11

At Home and Abroad

THERE was a man called Thórd Goddi,[1] who lived in Laxárdal north
of the river; his farmstead was called Goddastadir and has had that
name ever since. He was a very wealthy man, but had no children.
He had bought the land he was living on and was a neighbor of
Hrapp and was often made to feel it sorely. Hoskuld looked out for
him, so Thórd managed to hold on to his farm. Thórd had a wife by
the name of Vigdís; she was the daughter of Ingjald, Óláf Feilan's
son, and a niece of Thórd Gellir on her father's side and of Thórólf Rednose from Saudafell on her mother's side. Thórólf was a great fighting
man and had means. His kinsmen were in the habit of turning to
him for help. Vigdís had been given to Thórd in marriage more for
the sake of his money than for aid and support.

Thórd had a slave who had come out to Iceland with him; his
name was Ásgaut. He was a big man and capable; and even though he
was only a slave, there were few men free-born who could equal him.
He knew well the meaning of service to his lord and master. Thórd
had many slaves, although only this one is named here.

There was a man called Thorbjorn who lived in Laxárdal at the
next farm up from Thórd's place. He was nicknamed Skrjúp,[2] and
was a man of means, most of it being in gold and silver. He was a
man of big frame and great strength and was no squanderer on the
common folk.

To Hoskuld Dala-Kollsson one thing seemed to be missing on his
estate: the housing was not as good as he would like. So he bought a
ship from a man from the Shetland Islands which was drawn up at
Blonduós at the mouth of the river. He got his ship ready and announced that he intended to go abroad and that Jórunn was to take
care of the farmstead and children. They put out to sea and got a
good wind and made Norway somewhat to the south. They landed
at Hordaland, where the town of Bergen now is. Hoskuld laid his
ship up, for he had a host of kinsmen there, although they are not
mentioned here. At that time King Hákon was at Vík.[3] Hoskuld did
not go to see the king, as his kinsmen received him with open arms.
That whole winter everything was quiet.

CHART 8

The Kin of Óláf Feilan and His Sister Ósk

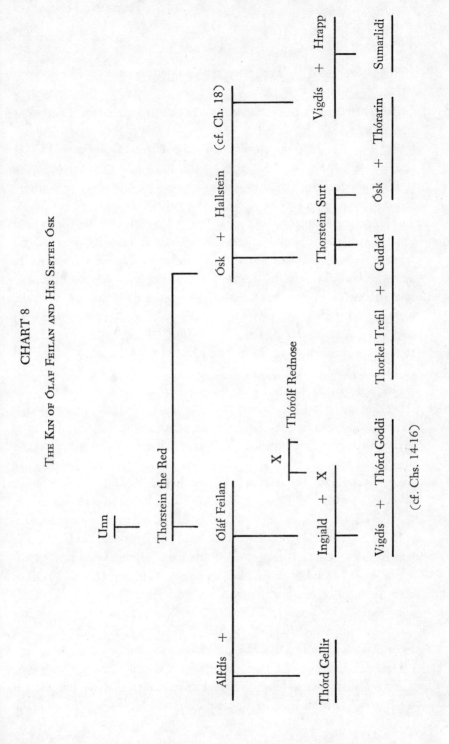

12

Three Marks of Silver

IT HAPPENED toward the beginning of summer that the king went
east to some islands called the Brenneyjar[1] on a military expedition
levied for the purpose of renewing the compact of peace for his
country, which in accordance with the laws was to be done every
third summer. This meeting was to be held among the chieftains to
settle such questions as came under the joint jurisdiction of the kings.
To attend this meeting was something of a holiday, for the people
came there from almost all the lands we have knowledge of. Hoskuld
launched his ship, for he too wanted to attend this meeting, especially
since he had not gone to see the king during the winter. One could
also visit a trading market there. The meeting drew a large crowd of
people, and there was much merrymaking — drinking and games and
all kinds of amusement — though nothing of any great importance
took place. But Hoskuld got to meet many of his kinsmen who lived
in Denmark.

One day when Hoskuld was on his way to enjoy himself with some
others, he spied a handsome tent a little apart from the other booths.
So he went over there and into the tent, where he found a man
sitting in velvet garments with a Russian hat on his head. Hoskuld
asked the man his name. "I am called Gilli," he said, "and many
would recognize me as soon as they heard the other name I am
known by: Gilli the Russian." Hoskuld said he had often heard him
spoken of, for he was supposed to be the wealthiest man who ever
had been in the league of merchants. Then Hoskuld said: "Maybe
you have the kind of thing for sale that we might like to buy." Gilli
asked what he and his companions were looking for. Hoskuld said he
wanted to buy a bondwoman — "if you have any to sell." Gilli
answered: "You seem to be trying to put me on the spot by asking
for something which you don't think I have on hand. But it remains
to be seen whether that is the case."

Hoskuld had noticed that there was a curtain across the booth.
Then Gilli raised the curtain and Hoskuld saw that twelve women
were sitting further back in the tent. Gilli told Hoskuld to go and take

a look and see if he wanted to buy any of these women. Hoskuld did so. They were sitting in a row across the back of the booth. Hoskuld looked the women over closely. He saw that one of them was sitting out toward the edge of the tent. She was poorly dressed, but he thought her lovely to look at, from what he could see. Then Hoskuld said: "How expensive would this woman be, should I want to buy her?" Gilli answered: "You'll have to pay three marks of silver for her." "It seems to me," Hoskuld said, "that you are setting a rather high price on this woman, for that is equal to the price of three." Gilli answered: "You are right in saying that I put a higher price on her than on the others. Why don't you choose another one and pay only one mark of silver for her and let this one remain in my keep?" Hoskuld said: "First I want to find out how much silver there is in the purse I have here on my belt." He asked Gilli to get the scales while he took a look in his purse.

Then Gilli said: "I want this deal to be made without guile on my part, for I want you to know this, Hoskuld, before we strike the bargain. This woman has an affliction." Hoskuld asked what that was. Gilli answered: "She is both deaf and dumb. I have tried in many ways to bring her to talk, but I have never been able to get a word out of her. I honestly believe she is unable to talk." Then Hoskuld said: "Bring out the scales and let's see what this purse here weighs." Gilli did so. They weighed the silver and it came to three marks. Then Hoskuld said: "It has now so turned out that this will be our bargain — you take this money and I will take the woman. I must say you have acted honorably in this matter, for you certainly did not want to be unfair to me." Then Hoskuld went home to his booth.

That same night Hoskuld went to bed with the bondwoman. The next morning when they were getting dressed, Hoskuld said: "There certainly isn't anything fancy about the clothes that wealthy fellow Gilli has given you. But of course it was harder for him to clothe twelve than for me to clothe one." Thereupon Hoskuld opened up a chest and took out some finery which he gave her. Everyone remarked that fine clothes suited her very well.

After the chieftains had discussed those matters which the law required, the meeting came to an end. Then Hoskuld went to see King

Hákon and addressed him with all due respect, as was only proper. The king gave him a sidewise glance and said: "We would have been glad to accept your salutation, Hoskuld, had it come somewhat earlier; but so be it anyway."

13

Bad Manners and a Fine Heritage

AFTER this the king received Hoskuld in all friendliness and invited him to go aboard his ship — "and stay with us as long as you want to remain in Norway," he said. Hoskuld replied: "I thank you most kindly for your offer, but I have much to do this summer. The main reason why I delayed so long in coming to see you was that I planned to get timber for house building." The king told him to sail along in to Vík. Hoskuld stayed with the king for some time, and the king got him house timber and had it loaded on his ship. Then the king said to Hoskuld: "I shall not detain you here with us any longer than you desire, but it won't be easy for us to get a man who can take your place."

Then the king saw Hoskuld off to his ship and said: "I have found you to be a man of honor, but if I don't miss my guess, this is the last time you will be sailing away from Norway while I am overlord here." Then the king pulled a ring of gold from his arm, one which weighed one mark, and gave it to Hoskuld; and he gave him another costly gift — a sword which was worth half a mark of gold. Hoskuld thanked the king for the gifts and all the honor which he had bestowed on him. Then Hoskuld boarded his ship and put out to sea.

They got a good wind and made the south of Iceland, and sailed on west around Reykjanes and up past Snaefellsnes and in at the Breida-fjord. Hoskuld landed at the mouth of the Laxá. He had his ship unloaded and laid up north of the river and built a shed there over it. One can still see traces of where it was built. There he set up booths, and the place is therefore called Búdardal (Boothdale). Then he had the timber moved home, which was easy, for it was not far. After this

Hoskuld rode home with some men and, needless to say, was given good welcome.

The property had been well taken care of in the meantime. Jórunn asked who the woman was whom he had brought along. Hoskuld answered: "You may think I answer jokingly, but I do not know her name." Jórunn said: "It will have to be one of two things — either the rumor that has come to my ears is a lie or you will have spoken with her at least enough to have asked her name." Hoskuld said that this he could not deny and told her the truth of it and asked that the woman be treated well, saying that it was his wish that she be at home there as a member of the household. Jórunn answered: "I don't intend to quarrel with your mistress, whom you have brought from Norway, even if she might not be good to have around; and now that seems all the more evident if she is both deaf and dumb." Hoskuld slept with his wife every night after he came home and had little to do with the bondwoman. It was apparent to everyone that she bore the stamp of a high-bred person and that she was no simpleton.

Toward the end of the winter, Hoskuld's concubine gave birth to a boy. Hoskuld was then called, and the child was shown to him. He, as well as everyone else, claimed they had never seen a nobler or more beautiful child. Hoskuld was asked what the boy was to be called. He said that he wanted him to be named Óláf, since Óláf Feilan, his mother's brother, had died shortly before.[1] Compared to most children, Óláf was an exceptional child, and Hoskuld showed great love for the boy.

The following summer Jórunn said that the bondwoman would have to take up some work or else leave. So Hoskuld asked the bondwoman to wait upon the master and mistress of the house and take care of her son at the same time. When the boy was two years old, he ran about alone and could say everything just like children of four years.

One morning when Hoskuld went to look around his farm — the weather was good, the sun was shining, but had not risen very high in the sky — he happened to hear the voices of people talking. He walked over to where a creek ran down along the slope. There he saw two people and knew at once who they were — Óláf and his mother. So he realized that she was not at all speechless, for she was talking a great deal to the boy. Then Hoskuld went up to them and asked her her name and said it would do no good for her to try to conceal it any longer. She said that she would not. They sat down on the slope and then she said: "If you want to know my name, I am called Melkorka." Hoskuld asked her to tell him more of her family. She answered: "My father's name is Mýrkjartan, and he is king in Ireland. I was captured and taken away when I was fifteen years old." Hoskuld said she had been silent altogether too long about such a fine lineage.

Then Hoskuld went in to tell Jórunn what news he had learned while making his rounds. Jórunn said she did not know whether there was much truth in what the bondwoman said and added that she had no liking for any such fairy folk, which ended their talk.

Jórunn was in no wise kindlier toward the bondwoman now than before, but Hoskuld was somewhat more so. One day shortly afterwards when Jórunn was going to bed, Melkorka was helping her pull her shoes and stockings off and put them on the floor. Jórunn took the stockings and began lashing Melkorka about the head with them, at which Melkorka got angry and gave her a blow on the nose with her fist, so that blood was loosened. Hoskuld came in and parted them. After that he sent Melkorka away and got a place for her to live up in Laxárdal. This farm was called Melkorkustadir and has had that name ever since. That place is now deserted; it lies to the south of the Laxá. There Melkorka set up housekeeping; Hoskuld got everything together that was needed, and their son Óláf went with her. It was soon apparent that Óláf would grow up to be a paragon among men, both in good looks and chivalrous manners.

14

The Undivided Catch

THERE was a man named Ingjald who lived in a group of islands in the Breidafjord called the Saudeyjar. He was called Ingjald Saudeyjargodi and was a wealthy man, prominent and able. His brother's name was Hall. Hall was a big fellow and had the makings of a man, but had little means and was considered rather useless by most people.

These two brothers were almost always in disagreement with one another. Ingjald thought that Hall showed little willingness to conform to the ways of accountable men, and Hall thought that Ingjald showed little willingness on his part to help him improve his lot.

There was a fishing station in the Breidafjord out at some islands called the Bjarneyjar. There are a number of islands together in this group, and the fish stock there was good. Men were in the habit of going there often to fish, and one could always find plenty of people out there all year round. Those of wise judgment thought it important for the men to get on well together out at the outlying fishing grounds. The fishermen used to say they had less luck in their catch if there were disagreements, and most heeded this well.

One summer, it is said that Hall, Ingjald Saudeyjargodi's brother, came to the Bjarneyjar to fish. He shared a boat with a man by the name of Thórólf, a Breidfirther who had next to nothing and was practically a tramp, but nonetheless an able man. Hall stayed out there for some time and put on airs of being better than anybody else.

One evening when Hall and Thórólf were coming in to shore and were to divide their catch, Hall wanted both to divide and choose shares, since he thought himself the better man there. Thórólf did not want to be worsted and used strong language. They exchanged some words over this, and each would only see it his way. Hall reached for a cleaver that was lying nearby and was about to drive it into Thórólf's head when men jumped between them and stopped him. Hall was extremely angry, but got nowhere with it that time; their catch, though, was not divided.

Now Thórólf stalked off that evening, and Hall alone took up the catch which they both owned, for the odds in strength told. Hall got another man in Thórólf's place in the boat and kept on with the fishing as before. Thórólf was ill content with his lot and felt he had been greatly put to shame by their dealings. Yet he stayed around there in the islands, his mind set upon straightening this hook that had been so uncomfortably bent for him. Hall had not the slightest misgiving, thinking that no one would dare challenge him in his own home district.

Now it happened one day when the weather was fair that Hall rowed out, three together in the boat. The fish were biting well that day, and they rowed home in the evening in high spirits. Thórólf, however, had been keeping track of Hall's doings during the day and was standing at the landing place in the evening when Hall and his men came in to shore. Hall was rowing in the forehold. Now Hall jumps out of the boat and is about to pull it in, but just as he leaps ashore, there Thórólf is standing ready and strikes him a blow. The blow lands at the base of his neck, and off flies Hall's head. Thórólf makes off after that, and Hall's comrades throng about the body.[1]

Now the news of Hall's killing spread throughout the islands, and it was thought grave, for the man was of high birth, even if not favored by fortune. Thórólf now tried to get out of the islands, for he knew of no one there who would shelter him after such a gross deed. Neither did he have any kinsmen from whom he could expect help. On the other hand there were those close by who were likely to make an attempt on his life — powerful men such as Ingjald Saudeyjargodi, Hall's brother.

Thórólf managed to get himself over to the mainland and moved on, keeping under cover. Nothing is told of his whereabouts and moves until he came one day toward nightfall to Goddastadir. Vigdís, Thórd Goddi's wife, was distantly related to Thórólf, and so it was that Thórólf turned in at this farm. He had heard before how matters stood there — that Vigdís had a stronger character than her husband Thórd. So the same evening that he got there, he went straightway first to see Vigdís and told her his troubles and asked her to help him. Vigdís replied: "Our kinship I cannot deny, but as for this deed you have done, the only thing I can say is that I don't consider you a worse man for it. But still it seems to me that anyone who helps you out will be risking both life and property, seeing what powerful men are bound to take up the prosecution of this case. And Thórd, my husband," she said, "is not much of a hero. And we womenfolk aren't much good either at thinking up expedients under stress. Still I'm not of a mind to leave you in the lurch altogether, since you did expect to get some help here." After that she led him out to a shed and told him to wait for her there, and drew a bolt across the door.

Then she went in to Thórd and said: "A man by the name of Thórólf has come here looking for lodging for the night. He is a distant relative of mine, and it looks as though he might need to stay here longer, if you will allow it." Thórd said he did not like people lingering around his farm, but that the man might rest up until the next day, if he was not mixed up in any trouble; otherwise he would have to leave directly. Vigdís answered: "I have already promised him overnight's lodging, and I don't intend to go back on my word, even if he isn't on exactly friendly terms with everybody." Then she told him about the killing of Hall and also that this same Thórólf who had come there was the one who had done it. Thórd flew into a rage at this and said he knew beyond a doubt that Ingjald would make him pay dearly for the sheltering they had already given him — "seeing how our doors have already been locked after this man." Vigdís answered: "Ingjald won't be taking your money for just one night's sheltering, for Thórólf is going to remain here all winter." Thórd said: "There's no surer way for you to strip me penniless, and it is against my will that such a hapless fellow should stay here." Yet Thórólf stayed on through the winter.

Ingjald, who was duty-bound to take up prosecution of his brother's killer, heard this and made ready to go to the Breidafjord Dales toward the end of winter. He launched a ferry of his, taking along a party of twelve altogether. They sailed east with a stiff northwester and landed at the mouth of the Laxá about nightfall. They drew the boat up on shore and went on to Goddastadir that same evening. Their coming was not unexpected, and they were well received. Ingjald took Thórd aside for a talk, giving as his reason for coming that he had learned that Thórólf, his brother's slayer, was there. Thórd said there was no truth in it. Ingjald told him not to deny it — "but let us two rather make a deal with one another: you hand over the man without my having to use force, and the three marks of silver I have here will be yours. I will also drop the charges you have brought upon yourself by sheltering Thórólf." The money looked tempting to Thórd, and besides Ingjald promised to drop those charges over which he had dreaded losing so much money. So Thórd said: "Now I will keep our talk covered up, but nonetheless this will be our bargain." They then slept until the night was nearly spent, and it was just a while before daybreak.

15

Good Guessing

THEN Ingjald and his men got up and dressed. Vigdís asked Thórd what he and Ingjald had been talking about the night before. He answered that they had been talking about many things and it had been agreed that there would be a ransacking, but that they would be cleared of the charges if Thórólf were not to be found there — "so I have had my slave Ásgaut lead the man away." Vigdís said she did not approve of lies and also did not like having Ingjald snoop around in her house, but said nonetheless it was up to him to decide. Then Ingjald ransacked the place and did not find the man there. Presently Ásgaut came back, and Vigdís asked where he had left Thórólf. Ásgaut answered: "I led him away to our sheep sheds as Thórd told me to do." Vigdís said: "What could be more directly on Ingjald's path back to his boat than this? But that risk is not going to be taken, whether it is the plan they hatched together last night or not. I want you to go at once and lead Thórólf away as quickly as possible. You are to take him to Saudafell, to Thórólf Rednose. If you do as I ask, you shall get something in return. I will give you your freedom and enough money so that you can go anywhere you like." Ásgaut agreed to this and went to the sheep sheds where he found Thórólf and told him that they would have to be off at once.

About this time Ingjald rode away from Goddastadir, for now he was intending to get his silver's worth. As they came down from the farmstead, he and his party saw two men coming toward them, and there was Ásgaut and Thórólf. This was early in the morning, so there was but little daylight. Now Ásgaut and Thórólf found themselves in a pinch, for Ingjald was on one side and the Laxá on the other. The river was very swollen and there were great masses of ice on both banks, and a swift, open current in the middle; so it was an ill matter to attempt a crossing. Then Thórólf said to Ásgaut: "Now it looks to me as though we are faced with two choices. One is to wait for them here at the river and defend ourselves as long as our strength and courage hold out, but chances are that Ingjald and his men will make quick work of taking our lives; the other is to take to the river, and that looks like a rather risky venture." Ásgaut said it was up to him and that he would not desert him now — "whichever way you decide." "Then we shall try for the river," said Thórólf, and they did so. They stripped themselves down as light as possible and then went out across the ice at the bank and plunged in for the swim. But since they were hardy men and since fate had destined them to live longer, they succeeded in getting across the river and up onto the ice on the other side.

They had just got across when Ingjald and his companions reached the bank on the other side. Then Ingjald spoke to his men: "What are we going to do now? Shall we make a try for the river or not?" They said it was up to him and that they would rely on his judgment, even though the river seemed unfordable to them. Ingjald said that was true — "and so we will have to quit the river and turn back."

As soon as Thórólf and Ásgaut saw that Ingjald and his men were not going to try to cross, they took time to wring out their clothes and got ready to be on their way, walking all day long until they came to Saudafell by nightfall. They were well received, for it was always open house there for all comers. And that same evening Ásgaut went to Thórólf Rednose and told him how matters stood and why they had come, and that his kinswoman Vigdís had sent this man to him for help and sheltering. He also told him everything that had happened between Ingjald and Thórd Goddi. Thereupon he brought out the tokens which Vigdís had sent by him for Thórólf. Thórólf replied this way: "I cannot refuse to acknowledge these tokens and will certainly take this man in at her request. To my mind Vigdís has handled this honorably; it is a great pity that a woman like her should get such a bad match in a husband. And you, Ásgaut, can stay here as long as you like." Ásgaut said he would not stay there very long. So now Thórólf Rednose took this namesake of his in and he became one of Thórólf's followers. He and Ásgaut parted good friends, and Ásgaut set out again for home.

But now to go back and tell of Ingjald. He had returned to Godda-stadir after he and Thórólf had come to the parting of the ways. In the meantime men had gathered there from the nearest farms at Vigdís' summons, and there were no fewer than twenty on the premises. When Ingjald and his men got to the farm, Ingjald called Thórd over to him and had this to say: "You have acted dishonorably toward us, Thórd," he said, "for we know beyond a doubt that you have let the man get away." Thórd said he was being accused unjustly in this. And now the whole agreement between him and Ingjald came out. Ingjald wanted to have the money back which he had paid out to Thórd. Vigdís was standing within hearing all during this talk and spoke up and said that each of them had got what was coming to him. She told Thórd not to keep the money — "for you, Thórd," she said, "have come by this money dishonorably." Thórd said she no doubt would have to have it her way.

Thereupon Vigdís goes indoors and to a chest which belonged to Thórd, and there at the bottom she finds a heavy money bag. She takes the bag out and goes out with it to where Ingjald is and tells him to take his money. Ingjald is all smiles and reaches his hand out for the purse. Vigdís flings the bag up in his face, striking him on the nose, so that blood falls onto the ground. On top of that she finds as many nasty words for him as she can and adds that he shall never get his money again and tells him to be off. Ingjald understands that the sooner he gets away the better, and so he goes and keeps on going until he gets home, ill-content with the whole affair.

CHART 9
Ólaf Peacock's Relation to His Foster Father Thord Goddi

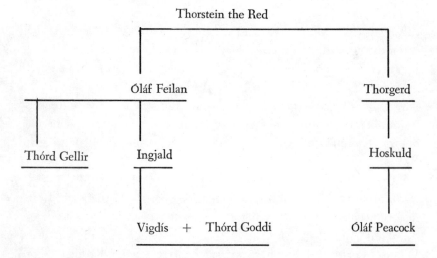

Thorstein the Red

Óláf Feilan   Thorgerd

Thórd Gellir   Ingjald   Hoskuld

Vigdís   +   Thórd Goddi   Óláf Peacock

16

Into Better Hands

ABOUT that time Ásgaut came home. Vigdís welcomed him and inquired how they had been received at Saudafell. He spoke very well of this and also told her what Thórólf Rednose's parting words had been. "You, Ásgaut," she said, "have done your errand well and faithfully; you shall now have that reward which you were promised.[1] I give you your freedom, so that from this day forth you shall be called a freedman. Moreover you shall have the money which Thórd took for my kinsman Thórólf's head. Now the money has fallen into better hands." Ásgaut thanked her with warm words for this gift. The following summer Ásgaut got himself passage on a ship at Dogurdarnes. That ship put out to sea, and they got heavy weather, but for all that, their crossing was not long and they made Norway. Thereafter Ásgaut went on to Denmark and settled down there and was thought a fine and valiant fellow. And here ends the story of him.

After the scheming of Thórd Goddi and Ingjald Saudeyjargodi to bring about the death of her kinsman Thórólf, Vigdís let it come to an open breach between her and her husband and declared herself divorced from him and went to her kinsfolk and told them the tale. Thórd Gellir — being the head of the family — did not take well to this, but nonetheless everything stayed quiet.

Vigdís had brought away from Goddastadir no more than her own valuables. The men at Hvamm let word get around that they intended getting half of the property which Thórd Goddi had in his custody. At this Thórd became very alarmed and rode at once to see Hoskuld and told him his troubles. Hoskuld said: "You have been panic-stricken before when you haven't had very much of a force to contend with."[2] Then Thórd even offered to pay Hoskuld for his assistance and added that he would not be niggardly about the cost. Hoskuld answered: "It is a well-known fact that you would never let anyone profit from what belonged to you, if you could help it." Thórd replied: "But it's not that way now, for I'm quite willing to hand over into your custody all my property. I also want to offer to foster your son Óláf and leave him all my property after my day, for

I have no heir in this country. Besides I think my money will have fallen into better hands than if Vigdís' kinsmen got their clutches on it." Hoskuld agreed to this and had the contract made binding. Melkorka took this very hard, for she considered the fostering beneath them, but Hoskuld said she just did not see it right — "Thórd is an old man and childless, and he means all his goods and wealth to go to Óláf after his own day, and you can always go to see Óláf whenever you like."

So Thórd took Óláf into his care when he was seven years old and was very fond of him. Those who had the suit against Thórd Goddi learned of all this, and now the recovery of the money seemed more difficult than ever. Hoskuld sent handsome presents to Thórd Gellir and begged him not to take offense at any of this, for legally they could not get any money from Thórd. He said Vigdís had brought no grounds against Thórd which were true and valid for a divorce — "and Thórd can't be called any less of a man for having tried to get rid of someone who had been thrust upon him and who was as beset with charges as a bramble bush with burrs." When these words from Hoskuld came to Thórd Gellir and valuable gifts along with them, he calmed down and said he thought that any property was in good hands which Hoskuld had charge of; and he accepted the gifts. After that the matter stayed quiet, but the friendship was somewhat cooler than before.

Óláf grew up with Thórd Goddi and became a big man and strong. He was so handsome that his equal was not to be found anywhere. When he was twelve years old, he rode to the Thing; and people thought it reason enough to have come from other districts just to marvel at him and how handsome a build he had. To match his natural prowess, Óláf outfitted himself in fine weapons and clothes, so that he was readily distinguished from all other men. Thórd Goddi's circumstances took a turn for the better after Óláf came to live with him. Hoskuld gave him a nickname and called him Óláf Peacock, and that name stuck with him.

17

A Watchful Eye

Now IT is said of Hrapp that he became so mean to deal with and molested his neighbors so much that they could scarcely hold their own against him. But he had not been able to get any hold on Thórd ever since Óláf had grown up. Hrapp never changed; he kept his same disposition, even when old age crept upon him and his strength gave out. Finally he had to take to his bed because of it. Hrapp then called his wife Vigdís to him and said to her: "I have never been ailing," he said, "but in all likelihood this illness is going to mean the end of our life together. And when I am dead, I want to have a grave dug for me under the doorsill of my fire-hall,[1] and I want to be placed standing down there in the doorway. I can then keep a more watchful eye on my household and property."

After that Hrapp died, and all was carried out just as he had requested, for Vigdís did not dare do otherwise. But mean as he had been to deal with when he was alive, it got to be even worse now that he was dead, for he walked about a great deal. People say that he killed most of his household in his hauntings. He caused a great deal of trouble for almost everybody in the neighborhood, and the farmstead at Hrappsstadir was left deserted. Vigdís moved west to her brother Thorstein Surt, who took her in with all her goods. Now it was just as before — people went to Hoskuld and told him about the trouble Hrapp was making for them and asked him to help them out. Hoskuld said he would and went with some men to Hrappsstadir and had Hrapp dug up and carried off to a place where both cattle and people were least likely to cross. After that Hrapp's haunting more or less let up.

Hrapp's son Sumarlidi inherited the land and property which his father had left, and it was both large and goodly. Sumarlidi settled down at Hrappsstadir the following spring, but he had not lived there long before he went mad and soon after died. Now his mother Vigdís became sole heir to all that property, but she had no desire to go back to the farm at Hrappsstadir; so Thorstein Surt took it into his custody.

He was at that time rather advanced in years, but nonetheless still very hale and hearty.

18

The Big-flippered Seal

AT THAT time Thorstein's kinsmen, Bork the Stout and his brother Thorgrím, were rising to rank and prominence in Thórsnes. It soon became apparent that these brothers were setting themselves up to be the most important and highly regarded men thereabouts. So when Thorstein saw how it was, he had no desire to vie with them and let it be known that he intended to change abodes and moved to Hrappsstadir in Laxárdal.

Thorstein Surt began his moving in spring after the Thing, and his livestock was driven down along the shore. Thorstein fitted out a ferry, and twelve of them altogether went aboard. There was Thórarin, his son-in-law, on board and also Ósk, Thorstein's daughter. Thórarin's daughter Hild was along too; she was then three years old. Thorstein set sail to a stiff southwester. They sailed into the fjord narrows and got into that channel which is known as the Kol-kistustraum,[1] the swiftest and strongest of the currents in the Breida-fjord. Their sailing was fraught with obstacles. In the first place, ebb tide had set in, and not only that, the wind was unfavorable, for the weather was squally, gusting to a sharp gale when the showers came on, but with scarcely any breeze between times. Thórarin was steering and had the sail braces around his shoulders, because the boat was crowded and tightly packed. It was mostly laden with crates and chests, and the cargo was piled high, and land was close by on either side. The ship made little headway, for a violent countercur-rent set in against them. Then they sailed up onto a rock, but for all that the ship did not break up. Thorstein ordered the men to drop sail as quickly as possible and to take poles and push the ship off. This they tried, but it was to no avail, for it was so deep on both sides that the poles could not reach bottom. So they were forced to wait for

high tide, and in the meantime the water ebbed out from under the
keel.

They caught sight of a seal in the channel during the day, one
much bigger than all the others. It swam in circles around the ship
throughout the day and it was a big-flippered one too. They all
thought it seemed to have human eyes.[2] Thorstein told his men to
shoot the seal, and they made a try at it, but that too came to nought.
Then the tide came in, and just as they were about to get afloat, a
sharp gust broke upon them and overturned the boat, and all on board
drowned, except for one. He was washed ashore with the timbers. His
name was Gudmund, and the islands where he landed have been
called the Gudmundareyjar ever since. Gudríd, the wife of Thorkel
Trefil, was now entitled to the inheritance after her father, Thorstein
Surt.[3]

The news of the drowning of Thorstein Surt and those who had
perished with him was told far and wide. Thorkel sent word at once
to this man Gudmund who had drifted ashore. And when he came to
see Thorkel, Thorkel struck a bargain with him in secret, telling him
to relate the story of the drownings in the way he, Thorkel, would

CHART 10

The Order of the Drownings in Thorkel Trefil's Inheritance Claim

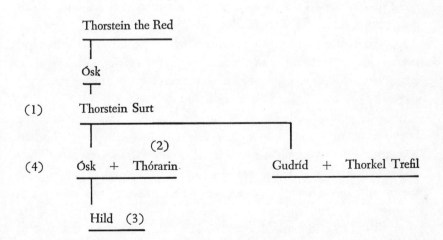

tell him beforehand. This Gudmund agreed to do. Thereafter Thorkel drew an account of the event from him and made sure that many people were within hearing, and Gudmund related as follows: Thorstein Surt had drowned first, then Thórarin, his son-in-law — that made Hild entitled to the property since she was Thórarin's daughter. Then the little girl drowned, he said — that made her mother Ósk the closest heir. And Ósk was the last one of all to drown, he said. In this wise all the property fell to Thorkel Trefil's lot, for his wife Gudríd was entitled to the property left by her sister Ósk.

Now this account was spread about by Thorkel and his people, but earlier Gudmund had told it somewhat differently. To Thórarin's kinsmen this tale seemed a bit dubious, and they said they would not put any store in it without some proof and claimed half the property for themselves along with Thorkel. But Thorkel maintained he was sole heir and asked for proof by ordeal according to their custom.

At that time such an ordeal consisted of what is known as going-under-the-sod. A strip of sod was cut loose from the soil, with the ends of it remaining firmly attached to the ground, and the man who was to perform the ordeal was to walk under it.[4] Thorkel Trefil rather had his doubts whether the drownings actually had happened in the way he and Gudmund had said the last time.[5] (Heathen men did not think they had less at stake when they were to go through such tests than Christian men do now when ordeals are performed. Whoever went under the sod was cleared of guilt if the strip of sod did not fall down upon him.) So Thorkel devised a plan with two men whereby they should pretend to get into a quarrel about something or other and be standing nearby when the ordeal was being carried out, and then come in so close to the strip of sod that everybody could see that they were the ones who caused it to fall in.

Now the one who was to carry out the ordeal gets started,[6] and just at the moment when he had come under the sod, the men who had been put up to this push at each other with their weapons. They meet one another near the arch of sod and throw themselves down there, and down comes the sod, as was expected. Some men run between them and separate them, which was easy, for they were not after all fighting in earnest. Thorkel Trefil then asked for the general opinion of the outcome of the ordeal. All his men agreed that it might have gone off well if no one had spoiled it. Thereafter Thorkel took over all Thorstein's personal property, but the lands at Hrapps-stadir were left to lie fallow.

19

An Inheritance Claimed

BUT TO get back and tell of Hoskuld. He was living in high estate and was a great chieftain. He had in his custody much property which belonged to his half brother, Hrút Herjólfsson. Many people said that it would cut quite heavily into Hoskuld's wealth if he were to pay out all of Hrút's inheritance from his mother.

Hrút belonged to the guard of King Harald Gunnhildarson and was highly regarded by him, mainly because he proved himself best in all tests of valor. And he stood in such high favor with Queen Gunnhild, that in her opinion no one in the guard could equal him, be it in word or deed. And whenever talk ran to the comparison of men and their merits, it was easy for everybody to see that Gunnhild ascribed it to stupidity or envy if any man was said to come up to Hrút. Now in view of the fact that Hrút had noble kinsmen and much property in Iceland, he was eager to go there and put in his claim and so made ready for a journey to that country. At parting the king gave him a ship and said he had proved himself a stalwart fellow. Gunnhild saw him off to the ship and said: "It need not be said in a whisper that I have found you to be a splendid man, for in prowess you are equal to the best in this land, and in wits you are far beyond them all." With that she gave him a gold ring and bade him farewell, drew her cloak over her head, and went swiftly home. Hrút boarded his ship and put out to sea.

He had good sailing and made the Breidafjord. He sailed up the fjord, through the islands and into the Breidasund and laid in at Kambsnes, where he let the gangplanks down. News of the ship's arrival spread abroad and also that Hrút Herjólfsson was the master. This news was not very welcome to Hoskuld, and he did not go to meet his brother.

Hrút drew his ship up ashore and laid it up. At this place he built

a farmstead, which has been known as Kambsnes ever since.[1] Then
Hrút rode to see Hoskuld and to claim his share of his maternal
inheritance. Hoskuld said he owed him nothing, and that his mother
had not left Iceland empty-handed when she went away and met
Herjólf. Hrút took this ill and said so, then rode away. All Hrút's
kinsmen treated him respectfully, except Hoskuld. Hrút lived at
Kambsnes three years and continued to put in his claim for the inheritance at the Things and other legal gatherings, and he presented his
case well. Most people said Hrút was quite within his rights, but
Hoskuld argued that Thorgerd had not been married to Herjólf
with his consent and declared that he was his mother's legal guardian.
And there the matter stood.

That same fall Hoskuld went to a feast at Thórd Goddi's. Hrút
heard about this and rode to Hoskuldsstadir twelve men strong. He
drove off twenty head of cattle and left like number behind. Then
he sent a man to Hoskuld to let him know where he could look for
his cattle. Hoskuld's housecarls leapt to their weapons, and word was
sent to the nearest neighbors. Altogether their party came to fifteen.
Each and every one rode as fast as he could. Hrút and his men were
not aware of the pursuit until they were nearly back at Kambsnes.
They dismounted at once and tied their horses and went over to a
gravel bank. Hrút said they would make a stand there, adding that
even though his claim against Hoskuld was making slow progress,
never should it be said that he had run away in the face of Hoskuld's
thralls.[2] Hrút's followers said the odds in men were against them.
Hrút replied he was not at all worried about that and declared that
the more there were of them the better, for just that much worse
would it fare with them.

The Laxdalers now jumped off their horses and made ready. Hrút
told his men not to mind the odds and darted out ahead on the
charge. He had his helmet on, sword drawn in one hand and shield
ready in the other. A better fighter in arms could scarce be found.
So enraged was Hrút then, that few could keep up with him. Both
sides fought well for a while, but soon the Laxdalers found they were
no match for Hrút, for he killed two men in one onslaught. The
Laxdalers then called for quarter, and Hrút said they certainly could
have it. Of Hoskuld's housecarls who were still on their feet all were

wounded, and four lay dead. Hrút too went home with some wounds, but his companions with few or none at all, for it was Hrút who had been out ahead in the thick of the fray. Ever since that time the place where they fought has been called Orrustudal (Battle Valley). Hrút then had the cattle slaughtered.

But to return to Hoskuld. He had quickly gathered together some men as soon as he heard about the cattle raid and rode home, arriving just at the time when his housecarls got back home. They said their errand had gone off rather badly. Hoskuld flew into a rage at this and said he was not going to put up with any more robbery and man-slaughter from Hrút. He gathered men together that whole day.

Then his wife Jórunn went to have a talk with him and asked him what he was planning to do. "I'm not planning much," he answered, "but I would certainly like to give people something else to talk about other than the slaying of my housecarls." Jórunn answered: "It's a monstrous deed you have in mind if you are thinking of killing such a man as your brother. There are those who say Hrút would have been justified in claiming his inheritance long before this. Now he has made it clear that he no longer wants to be pushed around like some bastard, and cheated out of what is his,[3] for after all he does have a birthright to it. Now he probably didn't make up his mind to provoke you into a fight before he was sure he could count on some support from bigger men, for I am told that messages very likely have been passing in quiet between Thórd Gellir and Hrút. It would seem to me that such things would be well worth taking into account. Thórd no doubt won't have anything against backing up a suit where the facts in the case are so plain. You know too, Hoskuld, that ever since the matter between Thórd Goddi and Vigdís came up, there hasn't been the same close friendship between you and Thórd Gellir as before, even though you in the beginning tried to stave off his enmity and that of his kinsmen by sending gifts. I also think, Hoskuld, that they feel you and your son Óláf have been bearing down rather heavily on them. Now it would seem to me wiser if you would make your brother an honorable offer, for as the saying goes, 'a hungry wolf is sure to strike.' Hrút, I daresay, will take this in good part. From what I've been told, he's a sensible man, and no doubt will see that this does credit to you both."

After Jórunn put it that way, Hoskuld calmed down considerably, for what she said seemed reasonable. Now men who were friends to both brothers acted as go-betweens and offered reconciliation to Hrút from Hoskuld. Hrút took this agreeably and said he certainly wanted to reach an understanding with Hoskuld, and that he had long been prepared to put their kinship in order as it ought to be, if only Hoskuld would grant him his just due. Hrút said he would also be willing to make good whatever wrongs he, for his part, had done against Hoskuld. So these matters were settled and sealed between the two brothers, Hoskuld and Hrút. From then on they lived in good kinship with one another.

Hrút busied himself with his farm and proved himself a man of much account. He usually did little meddling in things, but whenever he did have his hand in something, he wanted to have his way. Hrút later moved from his old place and lived until old age on a farm which has been called Hrútsstadir ever since. He had a temple there in his field, and traces of it can still be seen. That place is called Trollaskeid (Path of the Trolls) now, and a highroad goes past there.

Hrút married a woman by the name of Unn, daughter of Mord Fiddle. Unn left him, and out of that arose the quarrels between the Laxdalers and the Fljótshlíders.[4] Hrút had a second wife by the name of Thorbjorg; she was Ármód's daughter. Hrút even had a third wife, but we will not name her. Hrút had sixteen sons and ten daughters by these two wives,[5] and it is told how one summer when Hrút was at the Thing, fourteen of his sons were there with him. This is mentioned because it was thought a mark of great splendor and power. All Hrút's sons were accomplished.

20

Outwitted on Two Scores

HOSKULD now sat on his farm and old age began to creep up on him; his sons were then all grown up. Thorleik made his home on the farm at Kambsnes, and Hoskuld paid out to him his share of the family property. After that Thorleik took a wife, a woman named

Gjaflaug, the daughter of Arnbjorn, Backslider-Bjorn's son, and Thorlaug Thórdardóttir from Hofdi. It was a worthy match. Gjaflaug was a beautiful woman, prideful and vain. Thorleik was an unreasonable and hard person to deal with and very bold. There was no great friendship between the kinsmen Hrút and Thorleik.[1] Hoskuld's son Bárd was at home with his father. He took as much charge of things on the farm as Hoskuld himself. Not much is mentioned here of Hoskuld's daughters; nonetheless there are known to be descendants from them.

Óláf Hoskuldsson was also grown up by this time and was one of the most handsome men people had ever set eyes on. He outfitted himself in fine weapons and clothes. Melkorka, Óláf's mother, was living at Melkorkustadir, as was written before. Hoskuld began neglecting Melkorka's household more than he used to, and said that to his mind it was no less her son Óláf's concern than his. And Óláf said he would care for her as best he could. Melkorka felt that Hoskuld was acting disgracefully toward her and set her mind on doing something which he would not like any better. Thorbjorn Skrjúp had been the one who had given Melkorka the most help in the management of her farmstead and had even made her an offer of marriage when she had been living there only a short time, but Melkorka had coolly refused.

There was a ship drawn up at Bordeyr in Hrútafjord. Orn was the name of the shipmaster. He was a member of the guard of King Harald Gunnhildarson. Melkorka and her son Óláf had a talk next time they met and she brought up the subject of his going abroad and said she would like him to visit his noble kinsmen — "for I have indeed spoken truly when I said Mýrkjartan is my father and is king of the Irish. And as for passage for you, that can easily be had at Bordeyr." Óláf answered her: "I have talked this over with my father before, but he rather turned a deaf ear to it. And as for my foster father's means, he has more in the way of land and livestock than in ready Icelandic wares." Melkorka replied: "I'm not going to put up with your being called a bondwoman's son any longer. And if all that keeps you from going is the lack of means, then I would rather see myself marry Thorbjorn, if that would make you more inclined to this journey; for I have an idea that he will hand over to you as many wares as you think you need, if he gets to marry me. And what will make it even better is that Hoskuld won't be very happy on two scores when he learns about this — that you have left the country and I am married." Óláf said the decision was entirely up to her.

Shortly thereafter Óláf had a talk with Thorbjorn and said he would like to get some wares from him on a loan and would make it well worth his while. Thorbjorn said: "On one and only one condition will I do it, and that is if I get to marry Melkorka; in that case I rather imagine what is mine will be just as much yours as what is your own." Óláf said this then would be arranged, and they talked over with one another those things they wanted, and all this was to come about without anyone's knowledge.

Hoskuld asked Óláf whether he wanted to ride to the Thing with him. Óláf said he could not because of jobs to attend to on the farm, and said he wanted to have a sheepfold made down at the Laxá. Hoskuld was very pleased that Óláf liked to busy himself about the farm. So Hoskuld rode to the Thing, while at Lambastadir[2] everything was turned toward the wedding preparations. Óláf alone set the terms of the marriage agreement. He took out for himself thirty hundreds[3] in wares over and above the marriage settlement and was not to pay it back. Bárd Hoskuldsson was at the wedding and was party to all these agreements. When the feast was over, Óláf rode off to the ship and found the shipmaster Orn and took passage with him.

Before he and Melkorka parted, she handed Óláf a large gold finger ring and said: "This ring my father gave me as a teething gift,[4] and I daresay he'll recognize it when he sees it." Besides this she put into his hand a knife and a belt and asked him to give them to her foster mother, saying: "I don't think she will refuse to acknowledge these tokens." And lastly Melkorka said: "I have prepared you for your leaving home as best I know how and have taught you to speak Irish, so that it will make no difference to you wherever you happen to land in Ireland." After that they parted. A fair wind came up as soon as Óláf got to the ship, and they straightway put out to sea.

21

Olaf Peacock: Pride and Prowess

Now Hoskuld came home from the Thing and heard what had happened. He took it quite hard, but since his nearest relatives had had a part in it, he calmed down and let matters stand.

Óláf and those with him had a good voyage and made Norway. Orn urged Óláf to go to King Harald's court, and maintained that King Harald had bestowed great honor on those who were not half as accomplished as Óláf was. Óláf said he would take his advice. So Óláf and Orn went to the court and were well received. The king at once recognized Óláf from his kinsmen and invited him to stay. Gunnhild made much of Óláf when she found out that he was Hrút's nephew. There were some, though, who surmised she enjoyed talking to Óláf, relatives or no.

Óláf grew moodier as the winter wore on. Orn asked him what was troubling him. Óláf answered: "I have a journey to make west across the sea,[1] and it would mean a great deal to me if you would lend a hand so that this voyage could be undertaken this summer." Orn told Óláf not to be so keen on this; he said he knew of no ships westward bound. Gunnhild came over and joined in their talk and said: "Now you two are talking such as I have never heard you before, for each of you will only see it his way." Óláf gave Gunnhild a courteous welcome, but did not let their talk drop. After that Orn walked away, and Óláf and Gunnhild continued the conversation. Óláf told her what he wanted to do and how important it was for him to get the journey under way. He knew for a fact, he said, that Mýrkjartan was his mother's father. Then Gunnhild replied: "I will see that you are provided with the means for this journey so that you may go in as grand style as you like." Óláf thanked her for these words.

After that Gunnhild had a ship made ready and manned, and asked Óláf to state how many men he wanted to take along on his voyage. Óláf said sixty and added that it mattered a great deal to him that the crew appear more like warriors than traders. She said it would be so. Orn is the only one mentioned by name on this journey, other than Óláf himself. This crew was indeed well fitted out.

King Harald and Gunnhild accompanied Óláf to his ship and said their guardian spirit of good luck[2] would go with him as well as their friendship, which he already had. King Harald said this was no hard thing to say, for they could think of no man who had come from Iceland in their day who was more promising. Then King Harald asked how old he was. "I am now eighteen," said Óláf. "Men such as you are indeed very exceptional, for you are as yet but little past the years of childhood. You must be sure to come to see us as soon as you return!" Then the king and Gunnhild bade Óláf farewell, and he and his men got on board and put straightway out to sea.

They had poor sailing that summer. There was much fog and scarcely any wind, and the little breeze they did get was usually unfavorable. They drifted farther and farther over the open sea, and a sense of being lost at sea came over most of the men on board. At last the fog lifted and a wind blew up, and they hoisted sail. The question then arose as to how they should set their course for Ireland, and the men were not agreed on this. Orn differed with most of them, and they spoke against him and said he was confused and that those in the majority should rule. The decision was then put up to Óláf, but his reply was: "Those with better judgment should decide, for to my mind nothing could be worse than the advice of many foolish men when they all put their heads together." The matter seemed settled after Óláf had so spoken, and Orn decided the setting of the course from then on.

They kept on sailing night and day, but never got much wind. Then one night the men on watch jumped to their feet and shouted for all hands to be up and quick about it, for they had seen land so close ahead that they had nearly struck against it with the prow. The sail was up, and there was very little wind. The men jumped up immediately, and Orn told them to steer clear of the land if they could. Óláf said: "There's no chance for that now, for I see there are breakers just off the stern. So drop sail and be quick about it and let's wait and decide what to do when there is light of day and we can tell what land this is." Then they cast anchors, and they bit in right away.

There was much talk back and forth during the night as to where they might have landed. With the break of day, they saw that it was

Ireland. Orn then said: "I don't think we have landed at a good place, for this is far from those ports or trading centers where foreigners are said to be welcome, and besides we are sticking up out of the water like a stranded stickleback, and from what I know of the laws of the Irish, they can claim the goods we have along as theirs, for they call a ship drift goods even if it is less ebbed from the stern than we are." Óláf said there would be no danger of that. "But I did notice that people are gathering over on the land today. The Irish seem indeed to take more than ordinary interest in the arrival of our ship. I also noticed today at ebb tide that a river's mouth comes out by this headland, and the sea doesn't completely ebb away from there. If our ship isn't damaged, then we can launch our jolly boat and tow the ship over there."

It was clay bottom where the ship had been lying at anchor, so the planking had not been damaged. They succeeded in dragging the ship over to the river's mouth and cast anchor there. As the day wore on, a great throng crowded down to the shore. Two men got into a boat and rowed out to the ship. They asked for those in charge of the ship. Óláf spoke up and replied in Irish, the same as they spoke. But as soon as they heard that these were Norsemen, the Irish demanded the forfeit of their goods in accordance with their laws, and said that no harm would come to them before the king had given their case a hearing. Óláf answered that that might be the law if there were no interpreter along with the traders[3]—"but I can tell you truthfully that these are peaceable men; nonetheless we are not going to give in without putting up a fight."

Then the Irish let out a war whoop and waded out into the sea and intended to tow ship, crew and all to land. The water was not very deep and came only up to their armpits, or just to the waistline of the tallest. But there where the ship lay afloat, the bay was so deep that no one could touch bottom. Óláf told his men to get out their weapons and man the ship from stem to stern. They stood so thick that the whole ship was studded with shield upon shield, and from under the rim of every shield a spearhead stuck out. Then Óláf strode forward to the prow. He wore a coat of mail, and had a gilt helmet on his head; he was girded with a sword, its hilt chased in gold. In his hand he carried a barbed spear,[4] embossed and finely wrought, and before him he held a shield of red with a lion traced in gold. When the Irish saw this battle array, they were panic-stricken and it no longer seemed so easy a booty prize as they had thought. The Irish stopped their advance and huddled together in a group. A murmur of discontent arose among them, for it now seemed quite obvious that this was a ship of war, and that there might be more ships on the way. In all haste they sent word to the king; which was easy, for he was then but a short distance away at a feast. He rode at once with a body of men down to the ship.

The distance between the shore and where the ship lay afloat was well within hailing distance. Now and again the Irish had done some shooting at them, but Óláf and his men had come to no harm by it. Óláf was standing there in his array, as was described before, and many marveled at what an imposing figure this shipmaster was. However, when Óláf's shipmates saw such a large cavalry come riding toward them — and it was indeed a most valiant looking company — they fell silent, for they thought they had heavy odds against them. When Óláf heard this murmur of discontent among his crew, he told them to take courage—"for now there is good chance for our cause; it is their king, Mýrkjartan, whom the Irish are hailing."

The Irish then rode up so near to the ship that each party could hear what the other said. The king asked who the master of the ship was. Óláf gave his name and asked who the valiant knight was with whom he was speaking. "I am called Mýrkjartan," he replied. Óláf said: "Are you king of the Irish?" He answered that he was, and then asked Óláf for news of general interest. Óláf gave him a full account of the happenings which the king wanted to know about. Then the king asked where they had come from and whose men they were and questioned Óláf more precisely about his kindred than he had before, for the king found this man was proud and would say no more than he was asked. Óláf said: "It shall be made known to you that we started out from Norway, and that the men here on board are members of King Harald Gunnhildarson's guard. As for my family, this much can be said, my lord: my father lives in Iceland, his name is Hoskuld, and he is a man of high birth. Of my mother's kin I daresay you have seen more than I, for she is called Melkorka, and I have been told in good faith that she is your daughter, my lord.

That is what has prompted me to undertake such a long journey. It means a great deal to me how you reply to this."

The king fell silent and turned to confer with his men. Some were wise and cautious and asked the king how much truth was likely to lie in what this man said. The king replied: "One can easily see that this Óláf is a man of high birth, whether he is our kinsman or not, and that he can speak Irish exceedingly well." After that the king came forward and addressed Óláf: "Now I shall give you a reply. To you and all your shipmates I shall grant safe conduct; but as for this kinship you claim with us, there will have to be some more talk before I can give answer to that."

Then the gangplanks were put down and Óláf and his shipmates went ashore. The Irish marveled at how valiant these men were. Óláf greeted the king well, taking off his helmet and bowing down before him. The king received him courteously. They then resumed their talk, and Óláf presented his case anew, speaking both at length and eloquently. He ended by saying that he had there on his finger a gold ring which Melkorka had given to him at their parting in Iceland—"and she said that you, my lord, gave it to her as a teething gift." The king took the ring and looked at it, and his face turned very red. "This token is indeed genuine," said the king," but it is by no means less noticeable that you bear strong resemblance to your mother, so that one could very easily recognize you by that alone. Therefore I shall most certainly acknowledge your kinship, Óláf, with these men here who can hear what I am saying as witnesses. Furthermore I invite you to my court together with all your company. What honor you may receive will depend on what manly virtue I find in you after I have put your mettle to more of a test."

Then the king got them horses to ride and set men at seeing to their ship and taking care of the goods which they had. The king then rode in to Dublin, and everyone thought these great tidings — that there should be riding with him the son of his daughter who long ago had been carried off by pirates when she was only fifteen years old. But the one to whom this news meant the most was Melkorka's foster mother who then lay bedridden, broken down from both grief and old age. Yet she needed no cane when she went out to meet Óláf. The king said to Óláf: "Here now has come Melkorka's foster mother, and she will surely want to hear all you can tell her about Melkorka and how she has fared." Óláf went toward her with open arms and set the old woman on his knee and told her that her foster daughter was getting along very well in Iceland. Then Óláf put the knife and belt into her hands, and the old woman recognized these cherished things and wept for joy, and remarked that two things were certain — Melkorka's son was exceptional — "but no wonder, he comes by it naturally!" The old woman was in good health and spirits all that winter.

The king was given little peace, for at that time the lands in the west were continually being harried. Throughout the winter, the king had to drive off vikings and raiders. Óláf and all his company were along on the king's ship, and whoever came up against them found them a rather formidable band to deal with. The king took Óláf and his companions into counsel on all decisions, for he had found Óláf to be both wise and eager to be in the lead in all tests of prowess. When the winter was far spent, the king summoned a Thing, and it was well attended. The king stood up and had the following to say: "It is known to you all that last fall a man came here to us who is my daughter's son and is also high-born on his father's side. I have found Óláf to be a man of such exceptionally great prowess that his equal is not to be found among us. Therefore I wish to tender him my kingdom after my day, for Óláf is without a doubt better fitted to rule than my own sons." Óláf thanked the king kindly and with eloquent words for this offer, but said he would not care to run the risk of how Mýrkjartan's sons would like this after their father was gone. And he added that it would be better to have short-lived fame than long-termed shame. He said he wanted to go back to Norway as soon as it was safe to travel between the two countries. He also added that his mother would find little happiness in life if he did not come home again. The king left the decision with Óláf. After that the meeting broke up.

When Óláf's ship was all set to sail, the king saw him off and gave him a spear inlaid with gold and an embossed sword and many other things of much value. Óláf begged that he might take Melkorka's foster mother with him, but the king said there was no need of that; so she did not go. Óláf and his men boarded their ship and they all parted in greatest friendship. After that they put out to sea. They had a good passage and made Norway, and Óláf's voyage brought him much fame. He got some horses and set off with his companions to find King Harald.

22

High Aspirations

ÓLÁF Hoskuldsson came now to King Harald's court and the king was happy to see him and Gunnhild even more so. They begged him with many kind words to stay on with them, and Óláf accepted. So both he and Orn stayed with the king's guard. The king and Gunnhild bestowed more honor upon Óláf than they had upon any foreigner before him. Óláf gave the king and Gunnhild many rare treasures which he had acquired in western Ireland. At Yuletide King Harald gave Óláf an outfit of clothes cut from scarlet cloth. Óláf spent a quiet winter, but toward the end of spring he and the king had a talk with one another, and Óláf asked for the king's leave to go out to Iceland that summer. "I have noble kinsmen there whom I would like to go back and see," he said. The king gave him this answer: "It would be more to my liking if you would settle down here with us and take whatever position you yourself would like." Óláf thanked the king for offering him this honor, but said he would still like to go to Iceland, if that would not be against the king's will. Then the king answered: "This is not going to cause any ill will against you Óláf. Go you shall to Iceland this summer, for I see your heart is very much set on it. And you are not to trouble about getting ready; I shall take care of all that." With that they ended their talk.

King Harald had a ship launched that spring. It was a trading vessel, and it was a large and good ship. He had it loaded with timber and fitted out with full rigging. When it was all ready, the king had Óláf called and said: "This ship is to be yours, Óláf, for I do not want you to sail away from Norway this summer as anyone else's passenger." Óláf thanked the king with kind words for his generosity,

and made ready for his journey. As soon as all was done and the
wind was favorable, he put out to sea, parting from the king in
warmest affection.

Óláf had good sailing that summer and came into the Hrútafjord
at Bordeyr. News of the ship's arrival and also who the master was
soon spread abroad. Hoskuld learned of the coming of his son Óláf
and was very pleased and rode straightway north to Hrútafjord with
some men. Father and son were very glad to see one another, and
Hoskuld asked Óláf home with him, and Óláf said that he would
come. Óláf got his ship laid up and his goods moved south. This
done, he rode south in a party of twelve and on home to Hoskuldsstadir.
Hoskuld gave his son a warm welcome and his brothers also received
him fondly, as did all his other kinsmen. But it was he and Bárd
who felt the closest to one another. Óláf's voyage brought him much
fame, and his kinship was also generally made known — that he was the
son of the daughter of Mýrkjartan, king of the Irish. This was told
throughout the land, as well as all the honor great men abroad had
bestowed upon him. Óláf had also brought many wares along to
Iceland. During that winter he stayed with his father.

Melkorka soon came to see her son Óláf. He received her warmly,
and she had many questions to ask about Ireland — first and foremost about her father and other kinsmen. Óláf told her all she wanted
to know. Finally she asked if her foster mother was still living. Óláf
said she was indeed. Melkorka asked then why he had not wanted
to give her the pleasure of bringing her foster mother along to Iceland. Óláf answered: "They did not wish me to take your foster
mother away from Ireland." "Maybe so," she replied; but it was
plain to see that it was not to her liking.

Melkorka and Thorbjorn had a son, and his name was Lambi. He
was a big man and strong and like his father both in looks and disposition. After Óláf had spent the winter in Iceland and spring came,
father and son had a talk about their plans. "I have been wishing,
Óláf," Hoskuld said, "that a wife could be found for you and that
you would then take over the farm of your foster father at Goddastadir. There is still a good deal of wealth and much property there,
and you could then manage the farm and I would help you look after

things." Óláf answered: "I haven't given this any serious thought before, and I don't know who or where the woman might be that I would consider myself lucky in getting. You no doubt understand that I intend to aim high when it comes to the matter of a marriage. I also am quite sure that you would not have brought this subject up before you had thought of where it was to land." Hoskuld answered, "You have guessed right. There is a man by the name of Egil. He is Skalla-Grím's[1] son and lives at Borg in Borgarfjord. Egil has a daughter whose name is Thorgerd. She is the woman I have in mind to ask in marriage on your behalf, for she is the best match in all Borgarfjord and even farther. Besides, having the men from Mýrar for in-laws would undoubtedly be an asset to you." Óláf answered: "In this matter I will rely on your judgment. Such a marriage is wholly to my liking, if it can be carried out. But mind you, father, I will take it very ill if this proposal is brought up and nothing comes of it." Hoskuld said: "It's decided then, we shall take up this suit." Óláf said it was up to him.

It was now almost time for the Thing. Hoskuld set out from home, taking a large company with him. His son Óláf went along. They set up their booth, and there was a large gathering. Egil Skalla-Grímsson was there too. Everyone who saw Óláf could not help but remark how handsome he was and how noble his bearing. He was well outfitted in weapons and clothes.

23

A Rebuff

It is told how one day father and son, Hoskuld and Óláf, went from their booth to have a talk with Egil. Egil greeted them well, for he and Hoskuld were on good speaking terms. Hoskuld then brought up the marriage proposal and asked for Thorgerd's hand on Óláf's behalf. Thorgerd was also there at the Thing. Egil took the matter well and said he had always heard good reports of both father and son. "I also know, Hoskuld," Egil said, "that you are a man of noble birth and highly esteemed, and Óláf's voyage has brought him much fame. It is therefore no wonder that such men as you set your aim high, for Óláf certainly does not lack for lineage or good looks. But still this has to be talked over with Thorgerd, for no man will have the privilege of getting her without her consent." Hoskuld said: "I wish then, that you would take this up with your daughter, Egil." Egil said he would and went straightway to have a talk with her.

Egil said to her: "There is a man by the name of Óláf Hoskuldsson, and he is now one of the most famous men hereabouts. His father Hoskuld has broached the question of a marriage on behalf of Óláf and has asked for your hand. I have left the matter for you to decide, and I would like to know your answer. However, I would think it easy to answer such a proposal, for the match is a very creditable one." Thorgerd answered: "I have heard you say that you loved me best of all your children, but now it seems to me you don't really mean it if you want to marry me off to a bondwoman's son, no matter how handsome and well decked out he is!" Egil said: "You don't seem to be equally well informed about this as about other things. Haven't you heard that he is the son of the daughter of Mýrkjartan, king of the Irish? He is much higher born on his mother's side than on his father's, but even the latter would make it a fully worthy match for us." Thorgerd refused to be convinced, so with that their talk ended and each would only see it his way.

The next day Egil went over to Hoskuld's booth, and Hoskuld gave him good welcome. They took up their talk again, and Hoskuld asked how their suit had fared. Egil did not have much good to say of it and told how the whole affair had ended, saying it looked as though things had bogged down.[1] Hoskuld said it seemed so—"but anyhow I think you did the best you could." Óláf was not present during their talk. After that Egil left, and Óláf came and asked how the marriage proposal was faring. Hoskuld said things were slowed down on Thorgerd's account. Óláf said: "Now it is just as I told you, father, that I would take it ill if I got some abusive words in return. You had your way when this was brought up, but now I'm going to see to it that it isn't dropped here. For a truer word was never spoken—'Business left to others is food for the wolves.' I shall go at once myself to Egil's booth." Hoskuld said he could have it his own way.

Óláf decked himself out in the scarlet clothes that King Harald had given him. Now Hoskuld and Óláf set out for Egil's booth. Hoskuld walks on ahead, with Óláf right at his heels. Egil bids them welcome, and Hoskuld sits down next to him. Óláf remains standing and takes a look around. He sees a woman sitting on the cross-bench there in the booth; she is beautiful, noble looking, and well dressed. He is quite sure that this must be Thorgerd, Egil's daughter. So he goes over to the floor-bench and sits down beside her. Thorgerd gives this man a greeting and asks who he is. Óláf tells her his name and also his father's. "You perhaps find it bold of a bondwoman's son to sit down beside you and presume to talk to you." Thorgerd replied: "You no doubt mean that you have done more daring things than talk with women." This was how their talk together began and they kept on talking the whole day. No one listened to what they were saying, but before they finished, Egil and Hoskuld were called over. Then the matter of the proposal was taken up again, and Thorgerd turned the decision over to her father.

Now the matter was easily settled, and the betrothal took place right then and there. The Laxdalers were shown great honor, as the bride was to be married at their farmstead instead of hers.[2] The wedding feast was set for seven weeks before the end of summer at Hoskuldsstadir. After that Egil and Hoskuld took leave of one another, and father and son rode home to Hoskuldsstadir.

Then preparations for the wedding feast at Hoskuldsstadir got underway, and nothing was stinted, for there were plenty of provisions. The guests arrived on the day set, and the Borgfirthers were well represented. Egil was there and his son Thorstein. The bride was along with a select following from their own district. Hoskuld too had a large group of guests already assembled to receive them. The feast was a magnificent one and the guests were sent off with gifts. Óláf gave Egil the sword Mýrkjartan had given him, and Egil was delighted with it. Nothing else to speak of happened there, and everyone went home.

24

Hjardarholt

ÓLÁF and Thorgerd lived at Hoskuldsstadir and grew to love one another deeply. It was apparent to everyone that she was a very remarkable woman. Usually she took little part in things, but whatever she did have her hand in was bound to turn out the way Thorgerd wanted it. That winter Óláf and Thorgerd stayed in turns either at Hoskuldsstadir or at Goddastadir with Óláf's foster father. In the spring Óláf took the farm at Goddastadir entirely into his charge. That summer Thórd Goddi took sick, and that illness caused his death. Óláf had a mound raised over him on the headland called Drafnarnes which juts out into the Laxá. Thereabouts is an enclosure which is called Haugsgard.[1] From that time on men started flocking to Óláf and he became a great chieftain. Hoskuld by no means begrudged him this, for he liked Óláf to be consulted in all important matters. It was the stateliest farmstead in all Laxárdal, this one that Óláf owned.

There were two brothers then staying with Óláf, each of whom had the name Án. One was called Án the White, and the other Án the Black. A third man in Óláf's household was called Beinir the Strong. They were workmen of Óláf's and all three of them were stalwart men. Thorgerd and Óláf had a daughter named Thuríd.

Those lands that Hrapp had owned were lying waste, as was said before. Óláf thought this property was situated just right for him. One day he talked this over with his father and said that they should send someone to speak to Trefil and let him know that they would like to buy the lands at Hrappsstadir from him, as well as the other property included in the estate. This was easily arranged and the sale was concluded, for Trefil saw it was better to have a crow in the hand than two in the woods. This was the bargain made between them: Óláf was to pay out three marks of silver for the lands. That was really not an even trade, for the lands were wide and fair and very productive; and large salmon and seal grounds were included, and there was also a big woodland there.

Somewhat further up from Hoskuldsstadir, north of the Laxá,

there was a clearing in the woods, and it almost goes without saying that Óláf's stock tended to gather there in both good weather and bad. One fall Óláf had a farm built in this same clearing, partly from timber which had been felled there in the woods and partly from some he had got as driftwood. This was a stately farmstead. The buildings remained vacant during the winter, but the following spring Óláf moved over there. He got his livestock, which had greatly multiplied, rounded up beforehand — indeed at that time no one in all Breidafjord was richer in livestock than he. Óláf now sent word to his father that he should be standing outside to watch his train as he moved to his new farm and wish him well. Hoskuld said he would. Óláf made arrangements for the moving. The sheep, which were the shyest, were driven out ahead; then came the milk cows, and next the dry cattle, and lastly came the pack horses. The men were placed at intervals so that the stock could not stray out of line. The front end of the van was just arriving at the new farmstead when Óláf rode out of the farmyard at Goddastadir, bringing up the rear; and there was no gap in between. Hoskuld was standing out-side with his household.[2] Then Hoskuld called out that he hoped his son Óláf would fare well and said that good fortune would be his at his new dwelling place. "And it is near my guess that his name will long be remembered." Jórunn, his wife, said: "This bond-woman's son has enough wealth all right for his name to be remembered."

Just at the same time as the housecarls had got the packs down from the horses, Óláf rode into the farmyard. "Now," he said, "I'm going to satisfy everyone's curiosity about something that has been the subject of talk all winter, namely what this farmstead is to be called. It shall be called Hjardarholt (Herdholt)." Everyone thought he had hit upon a good name, in view of the purpose the place had served.[3]

Óláf set up his household at Hjardarholt, and it soon became a stately farmstead, and there was not a thing that it lacked. Óláf now enjoyed even greater esteem. This was due to several things — he was very popular with people, for whenever he took charge of others' affairs, matters always turned out to their liking; and not only did his father contribute much to his being well thought of, his kinship with the men of Mýrar was also a great asset. Of all Hoskuld's sons, Óláf was considered the worthiest.

The first winter that Óláf lived at Hjardarholt, he had many servants and workmen, and the work was divided among them. Some tended the dry cattle and others the milk cows. The cow shed was out in the woods, quite some distance from the house. One evening the man who tended the dry cattle came to Óláf and asked him to get another man for that job — "and set me at another task." Óláf answered: "I want you to keep on with what you're doing." The man said he would sooner go away. Óláf said: "You seem to feel something is amiss. Now I will go with you this evening when you tie up the cattle, and if I think there's some excuse for this, then I'll not blame you; otherwise you'll be made to feel what accepting your lot means."

Óláf took his gold-chased spear, Mýrkjartan's gift, and he and his servant set out from home. There was a light snow on the ground. They came to the cow shed and found it open. Óláf told the cowhand to go in — "and I will drive the cattle in and you tie them up." The servant went to the door of the shed, but before Óláf knew it, the man had dashed back into his arms. Óláf asked why he was so frightened. He answered: "Hrapp is standing at the cow-shed door and tried to get hold of me, but I've had my fill of wrestling with him." Óláf now went up to the door and thrust his spear in at him. Hrapp took hold of the socket of the spear shaft with both hands and twisted it so that the shaft broke off. Just when Óláf was about to run at Hrapp, he disappeared straight down into the place whence he had come, and that was the parting of their ways. Óláf had the shaft and Hrapp the spearhead. After that Óláf and the cowhand tied up the cattle and then they went home. Óláf told the servant that he would not blame him for his complaining. The following morning Óláf set out from home to the place where Hrapp had been buried and had him dug up. Hrapp was still undecayed. Óláf found his spearhead there too. Then he had a pyre made and had Hrapp burned on it and his ashes carried out to sea. After that no man ever came to any harm again because of Hrapp's ghost-walking.

CHART 11

Hoskuld's Kin Marries into the Line of Bjorn the Eastman

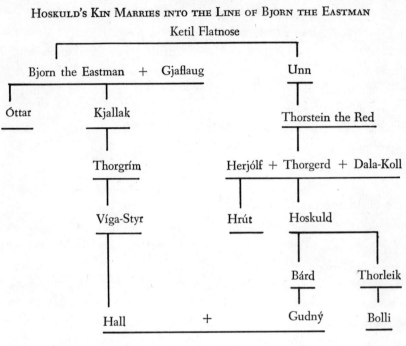

25

Boundary Troubles

BUT NOW to tell of Hoskuld's sons. Thorleik Hoskuldsson had been a great seafaring trader and had stayed with high-born men while on his trading voyages before he settled down on a farm. He was thought a man of some mark. He had also taken part in viking expeditions and proven himself in deeds of manliness. Bárd Hoskuldsson had also been a seafaring trader and had been well thought of wherever he went, for he was the best of fellows and a moderate man in everything. Bárd took as his wife a Breidafjord woman named Ástríd; she came of good stock. Bárd's son was called Thórarin, and his daughter's name was Gudný. Hall, Víga-Styr's son, was married to her and from them has come a great line of descendants.[1]

Hrút Herjólfsson had given a slave of his by the name of Hrólf his freedom, along with some property and a dwelling place at the border between his and Hoskuld's lands. But the boundary lay closer to Hrútsstadir than Hrút and his sons had thought, and failing to notice this, they had settled the freedman down on Hoskuld's land.[2] He soon prospered and grew wealthy there. Hoskuld ill liked Hrút's settling this Hrólf right under his nose, and he asked the freedman to pay him for the land he was living on — "for it belongs to me." The freedman went to Hrút and told him the whole story. Hrút told him to pay no attention and to give Hoskuld nothing. "I am not sure," he said, "which of us two really did own that land."

So the freedman went home and remained on his farm just as before. Soon thereafter Thorleik Hoskuldsson took his father's advice and rode with some men to the freedman's farm; there they seized and killed him. Thorleik claimed for himself and his father all the wealth which the freedman had amassed. This news reached Hrút and his sons, and they did not like it at all. Most of Hrút's sons were grown men, and such a host of kinsmen presented what seemed an unassailable bulwark. Hrút sought the law in proceeding with the case. But when those versed in the law looked into it, the verdict fell against Hrút and his sons, for the lawmen took considerable account of the fact that Hrút had settled the freedman down on Hoskuld's land without his consent, and that the freedman had prospered there. Thorleik had indeed killed him on his and his father's own property.

Hrút was ill-content with his lot, but nonetheless the matter rested there. After this Thorleik had a farm built at the boundary between Hrút's and Hoskuld's property, and that is called Kambsnes. There Thorleik lived for a while, as was told before.[3] Thorleik had a son by his wife. The boy was sprinkled with water and called Bolli. He soon grew up to be a fine and most promising lad.

26

Twelve Ounces

IN HIS old age Hoskuld Dala-Kollsson took sick. He sent for his sons and other kinsmen, and when they came, Hoskuld spoke to the brothers Bárd and Thorleik: "I have taken some illness, and as I have never been ailing, I think it will mean the death of me. Now as you know, you two are the legitimate heirs and have the right to take all the inheritance after my day, but there is a third son of mine who was not born in wedlock. I want to make a request of you two brothers that Óláf be included in the inheritance and divide with you in thirds." Bárd answered first and said he would do as his father wished — "for I look to Óláf to do me all the more honor the richer he is." Then Thorleik spoke: "It is far from my wish that Óláf be brought in as heir with us. Óláf is wealthy enough as it is. You, father, have given him much of what you owned and have shared unequally with us brothers long enough. I will not voluntarily give up the rights due to me by birth." Hoskuld said: "You two surely won't deprive me of my lawful right of giving twelve ounces to my son,[1] as high-born on his mother's side as Óláf is." To this Thorleik agreed.

Then Hoskuld called for his gold ring, King Hákon's gift; that weighed one mark. And then he called for his sword, also a gift from the king, and that was worth half a mark of gold. Both of these he gave to his son Óláf and wished him and his kinsmen good luck, adding that his reason for doing so was not out of ignorance of the fact that this luck had already found its way to him. Óláf accepted the gifts and said he would take his chances with how much Thorleik liked it. Thorleik was ill-content with this and thought Hoskuld had dealt underhandedly with him. Óláf told him: "I am not going to give up the gifts, Thorleik, for you gave your consent to this in the presence of witnesses. I'll take the risk of whether I'll get to keep them." Bárd said he would comply with his father's wishes.

After this Hoskuld died. That seemed a great loss, first and foremost for his sons, but also for all his relatives and friends. His sons had a befitting mound raised over him, and the brothers started talking

about preparing a funeral feast in their father's memory, for such
was the custom at that time. Then Óláf said: "I don't think we should
be in too great a hurry about preparing this feast, if it is to be as befitting as we would like. It is now far into the fall, and it is not easy to
procure provisions for a feast. And besides, most people will find it
difficult to travel in the fall of the year, especially those who have a
long journey, and we can only expect that many wouldn't be able to
come whom we would most like to have. So I will take it upon myself
to do the inviting to this feast at next summer's Thing and will put
up one third of the cost." This the brothers agreed to, and Óláf went
on home.

Thorleik and Bárd divided their father's property between them.
Bárd got the estate and the lands, for most people were in favor of
having it this way, as Bárd was the more popular one of the two.
Thorleik got the greater portion of the chattels. The brothers Bárd
and Óláf got on well together, but between Óláf and Thorleik there
was something of coolness.

Now the winter drew to a close, summer came, and time for the
Thing, and Hoskuld's sons made ready to go. It was soon apparent
that Óláf would be the foremost of the brothers. When they arrived
at the Thing, they covered over their booth and fixed it up in fine
and stately fashion.

27

Óláf's One-Third

IT IS told how one day when the men were going to the Law Rock,
Óláf stood up and asked for a hearing and first of all informed the
people of his father's decease. "Many of you here are both his kinsmen and friends. Now, it is the wish of my brothers that I announce
a funeral feast in memory of Hoskuld, our father, and invite all of
you with the rank of *godi,* for that will include most of you notable
men who are related to him by blood or marriage. I am also to make
known that none of the prominent guests shall go away without gifts.
Along with these people, we wish to invite the farmers and everyone

who wants to accept, rich and poor alike. And everyone shall come
for half a month's feast at Hoskuldsstadir when there are yet ten
weeks before winter." At the end of Óláf's speech there was big applause, and every one thought he had discharged his bidding mag-
nificently.

When Óláf came back to the booth, he told his brothers what he
had in mind, but they were little pleased with it and thought he had
carried things rather far. After the Thing the brothers rode home.
Now the summer wore on, and Óláf and his brothers prepared for the
feast. Óláf put out a good third for it; the best of everything was provided, and many stores were laid in, for they expected a great number
would come. When it was time for the feast, almost all the prominent men who had accepted came. It is generally agreed that the
number of guests did not fall far short of nine hundred. That makes
this feast the next largest ever to have been held in Iceland, second
only to the funeral feast which the sons of Hjalti gave in memory of
their father, where there were twelve hundred guests. The feast given
by Hoskuld's sons was a most magnificent one in every respect, and
the brothers gained much honor by it; but Óláf was thought the foremost of them. In the giving of gifts, he gave just as much as his two
brothers put together, and no prominent guest left without one.

When most of the guests had departed, Óláf turned to his brother
Thorleik and said: "You well know, kinsman, that as things stand,
there hasn't been much love lost between us. I would like to suggest
that we get on better terms. I know you disliked it when I accepted
those gifts from my father on his death day. Now since you feel
slighted by this, I would like to regain your good will by fostering
your son for, you know, he who fosters another's child is always
counted the lesser man." Thorleik took this well and said — as was
certainly true — that this was an honorable offer. So Óláf took Thorleik's son Bolli into his care. He was three years old at that time.
Óláf and Thorleik parted in kindliest affection, and Bolli went home
to Hjardarholt with Óláf. Thorgerd received him warmly and Bolli
grew up there, and they loved him no less than their own children.

CHART 12

ÓLÁF PEACOCK'S CHILDREN AND THE RELATION
OF THE FOSTER BROTHERS KJARTAN AND BOLLI

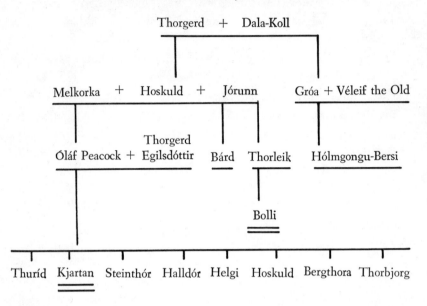

28

Youths of Promise: Kjartan and Bolli

ÓLÁF AND Thorgerd had a son. The boy was sprinkled with water
and given a name. Óláf had him called Kjartan after Mýrkjartan,
Óláf's maternal grandfather. Bolli and Kjartan were almost the same
age. And Óláf and Thorgerd had many other children; another son
of theirs was called Steinthór, another Halldór, and another Helgi.
Hoskuld was the name of the youngest of Óláf's sons. Bergthóra and
Thorbjorg were the names of Óláf's daughters. All of their children
showed promise as they grew up. At that time Hólmgongu-Bersi was
living in Saurbaer at the farmstead called Tunga; he went to see Óláf
and offered to foster his son Halldór. Óláf accepted this offer and
Bersi took Halldór home with him. He was then one year old. That
summer Bersi took sick and lay abed almost all summer long.

It is told that one day the men were out haying at Tunga, and these two, Halldór and Bersi, were left alone indoors. Halldór was lying in his cradle, when suddenly the cradle fell out from under him and dumped him onto the floor. Bersi was unable to get to him. Then Bersi spoke this ditty:

> Here we two lie
> In helpless plight
> Halldór and I,
> Not at all spry;
> Old age hinders me
> And infancy thee.
> 'twill mend with thee,
> But ne'er for me.

Then some men came to pick Halldór up from the floor, and Bersi got better. Halldór grew up there and became a big man, strong and sturdy.

Kjartan Óláfsson grew up at home in Hjardarholt. He was one of the most handsome men ever to have been born in Iceland. He had a large face with well-formed features, the finest of eyes and a light complexion. His hair was long and as fair as silk, and it fell into curls. He was a big man and strong, just as Egil, his mother's father, had been or his uncle Thórólf. Nature had endowed Kjartan with more gifts than most people, and all who saw him marveled at him. He was more skilled in arms than most, remarkably dextrous, and the best of swimmers. In fact he outshone other men in all sports. At the same time he was more modest than most, and was so well liked that even children were fond of him. He was lighthearted and generous. Of all his children Óláf loved Kjartan the best.

Bolli, his foster brother, was also a big man. He came next to equaling Kjartan in all sports and accomplishments. He too was strong and handsome, had a chivalrous and gallant manner, and liked fine clothes and weapons. These two foster brothers were very fond of one another. And so now Óláf sat contentedly at home on his farmstead, and the years rolled by.

29

A Generous Norwegian

ONE SPRING Óláf informed Thorgerd that he intended to go abroad
—"and I want you to look after the farmstead and children," he said.
Thorgerd said it was not very much to her liking, but Óláf said he
was the one to decide. He bought a ship which was drawn up at
Vadil in the west.

Óláf set sail during the summer and came with his ship to Hordaland.[1] There not far inland lived a man who was called Geirmund
the Noisy, a powerful man, wealthy, and a great viking. He was an
unreasonable and hard man to deal with. He had now settled down
and belonged to the guard of Earl Hákon the Mighty. Geirmund
went out to the ship and it did not take him long to strike up an
acquaintance with Óláf, for he had heard about him before. Geirmund invited Óláf home with as many men as he wanted to bring
along. Óláf accepted and went for a stay, taking five others along.
Óláf's oarsmen found themselves quarters round about Hordaland.
Geirmund treated Óláf well. He had a big, fine farm, and there
were lots of people there and plenty of merriment all winter long. But
when the winter was drawing to a close, Óláf told Geirmund that he
had come in order to procure some house timber for himself. He said
he put much store in getting good, choice timber. Geirmund answered: "Hákon the Earl has the best forests, and I know beyond a
doubt that if you go to see him, his woods will be at your disposal,
for many who aren't half as accomplished as you, Óláf, are given
good welcome whenever they come to see him."

So in the spring Óláf set out to pay Earl Hákon a visit. The earl
received him very cordially and asked Óláf to stay with him as long
as he liked. Óláf told the earl what had brought him there — "I would
like to make a request of you, my lord, to let me use your forest for
cutting house timber." The earl answered: "You won't find us
stingy, no matter how much timber you stow aboard, for it's not
every day we get such men as you coming from Iceland to visit us."
At parting the earl gave him an axe chased in gold, and it was a most
costly thing. They parted in kindliest affection.

Geirmund meanwhile had quietly been making arrangements for his lands and property and was planning to sail out to Iceland on Óláf's ship. He had kept this a secret from everyone. Even Óláf knew nothing of it until Geirmund had already moved his goods out to his ship; and that amounted to something of a fortune. Óláf said: "You wouldn't be going on my ship now, had I known this before, for I suspect there are going to be some people in Iceland who would be better off if they never set eyes on you. But now that you have already come down here with so much wealth, I can't bring myself to chase you off like a common cur." Geirmund said: "There's going to be no dissuading me for all your big words, for I fully intend to pay my way as your passenger."

Óláf and all the others boarded the ship and put out to sea. They had good sailing and made the Breidafjord. They ran the gangplanks ashore at the mouth of the Laxá, and Óláf had the timber brought ashore and the ship put up in the shed his father had built there. Óláf asked Geirmund home with him. That summer Óláf had a guesthouse built at Hjardarholt, bigger and better than anyone had ever seen. There were famous tales depicted on the wainscot and on the ceiling. These were so well done that people thought the hall even more handsome when no tapestries were hung.

Geirmund usually took little part in things and was unfriendly toward most people. He always went around dressed in a scarlet kirtle with a grey cloak over it, a bearskin cap on his head and a sword in his hand. This sword was a large weapon, and a good one, with a hilt made of walrus tusk. It had no silver-chased work, but its blade had a keen edge, and there was never a spot of rust on it. This sword he called Footbite, and he never let it very far out of his sight.

Geirmund had been there but a short time when he fell in love with Thuríd, Óláf's daughter, and approached Óláf with a marriage proposal, but Óláf refused him. Geirmund then turned to Thorgerd with bribes in order to bring about the match. She accepted his money, for it was no small amount he put out. Presently Thorgerd broached this subject to Óláf and said that in her opinion their daughter could not be married off better — "for he is a dauntless fellow, rich, and generous too." Then Óláf answered: "I will no more oppose your wishes in this than in anything else, even though

I would rather have married Thuríd off to someone else." Thorgerd walked away, self-satisfied with her errand.

Now she told Geirmund how matters stood, and he thanked her for her help and clever handling of the affair. Geirmund then took the marriage proposal up with Óláf again, and this time it was easily won. Thereupon Geirmund was betrothed to Thuríd and the wedding was to be held toward the end of winter at Hjardarholt. There was a large gathering at the wedding feast, for the guesthouse was finished by then. Úlf Uggason was at the wedding and he had made a poem about Óláf Hoskuldsson and about those tales that were depicted on the walls of the hall. He recited these verses at the feast. This poem is called Húsdrápa (The House Poem) and is well done. Óláf rewarded him generously for the poem. He also gave fine gifts to all the prominent men who had come. Óláf, it was thought, gained great honor from this feast.

30

Vengeance for Vengeance

THERE was not much love lost in Geirmund's and Thuríd's married life, and that was so on both sides. Geirmund had stayed with Óláf but three winters when he wanted to go away and announced that Thuríd was to stay behind together with their daughter Gróa, who was then one year old. But Geirmund refused to leave any money behind for their support. This found little favor with mother and daughter and they told Óláf so. But Óláf remarked: "What's this now, Thorgerd, isn't the Norwegian just as generous now as in that fall when he asked you for your daughter's hand?" They got nowhere with Óláf, for he was in all things a peaceable man. He said too that the little girl should stay on with them until she had grown up and knew how to get along on her own. And when he and Geirmund came to parting, Óláf gave him his trading vessel, completely fitted out. Geirmund thanked him very much and said it was a most generous gift. Then he made the ship ready and sailed out from the mouth of the Laxá with a light northeasterly wind, but when they came out by the islands, the wind died down. He lay out by Oxnaey half a month, for no fair wind came up for him to get under sail.

About that time Óláf had to leave home to look after the driftwood on his beaches. Then his daughter Thuríd called together some of the housecarls and bade them accompany her. She also took the little girl along. There were ten of them in all. She had Óláf's ferry launched and told the men to hoist sail and row out along the Hvammsfjord. When they came out by the islands, she asked them to lower a boat that was on the ferry. Thuríd climbed down into the boat and two men with her. She told those who were left behind to guard the ship until she came back. She took the little girl in her arms and told them to row across the channel to where they could get near Geirmund's ship. She took up an augur from the boat's locker and handed it to one of the men, telling him to get over to the ship's jolly boat and bore a hole in it, so that it would be disabled, should they have to use it in a hurry. Then she had herself put ashore, and she still had the little girl in her arms. This was at sunrise. She walked up the gangplank and onto the ship; all the men were sound asleep. She tiptoed over to the hammock where Geirmund lay sleeping. The sword Footbite was hanging on a peg. Thuríd laid Gróa in the hammock, snatched up Footbite, and took it with her. Then she left the ship and went back to her companions.

Soon the little girl began to cry. Geirmund woke up at this, sat up, recognized the child and seemed to know what lay at the bottom of it. He jumps to his feet, is just about to reach for Footbite but, needless to say, finds it missing. He goes over to the side rail just in time to see Thuríd and her companions rowing away from the ship. Geirmund orders his men to jump into the jolly boat and row after them. They do so, but when they had gone but a little way, they saw coal-black sea water pouring in; so they turned back. Then Geirmund calls out to Thuríd to come back and return Footbite — "and take your daughter with you and as much money as you like." Thuríd called back: "So you'd really be happier to have your sword back, would you?" Geirmund answered: "I'd rather part with almost anything before I'd be happier without it." Thuríd retorted: "Never shall you get it then! You have acted dastardly toward us on many a count, so now it's all finished between us." Then Geirmund said: "No good will come of your having this sword in your keep." Thuríd said she would take her chances with that. "In that case," says Geirmund, "may this sword cause the death of that man in your family who would be the greatest loss, and may this his death come about in a way most unbefitting."

After this Thuríd went home to Hjardarholt. Óláf had also come home by then and was anything but pleased by what she had done, but nonetheless let matters rest. Thuríd gave the sword Footbite to her kinsman Bolli, for she was no less fond of him than of her own brothers. Bolli carried this sword for a long time to come.

Presently Geirmund got a fair wind, and they put out to sea and made Norway in the fall. One night they sailed onto breakers out by Stad. Geirmund and all his crew perished, and that is all there is to say of him.

CHART 13

The Kin of Óláf Peacock's Three Daughters Thuríd, Thorbjorg, and Bergthóra

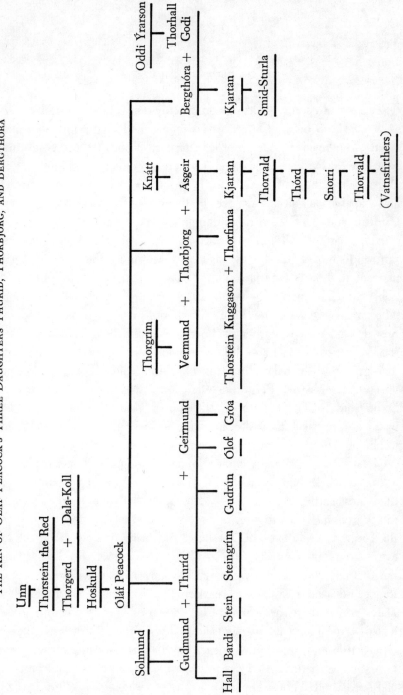

31

The Four-horned Ox

ÓLÁF Hoskuldsson was sitting contentedly on his farm, in high estate, as was written before. There was a man called Gudmund Solmundarson, who lived at Ásbjarnarnes north in Vídidal. This Gudmund was a wealthy man. He sued for Thuríd's hand and got her in marriage together with a rich dowry. Thuríd was wise, proud-minded, and capable. Their sons were Hall, Bardi, Stein, and Steingrím. Gudrún and Ólof were their daughters.

Óláf's daughter Thorbjorg was an unusually handsome woman, fair, and stout of build; she was called Thorbjorg the Stout and was married to Ásgeir Knattarson in Vatnsfjord in the west. He was a noble and fine man. Their son was Kjartan, who was the father of Thorvald, who was the father of Thórd, who was the father of Snorri, who was the father of Thorvald. From them have descended the Vatnsfirth kin. Later on Thorbjorg was married to Vermund Thorgrímsson; their daughter was Thorfinna whom Thorstein Kuggason took as a wife. Bergthóra Óláfsdóttir was married out west in Djúpafjord to Thórhall Godi, the son of Oddi Ýrarson. Their son was Kjartan, the father of Sturla the Smith;[1] Kjartan was the foster father of Thórd Gilsson, who was the father of Hvamm-Sturla.

Óláf Peacock had many choice animals among his livestock. He had a fine ox which had the name Harri,[2] dappled grey of coat and larger than most cattle. Harri had four horns; two of them were large and nicely grown, the third one, however, stood straight up in the air and the fourth grew out of his forehead and hung down in front of his eyes. That one was his "brunnvaka."[3] He scraped his hoof like a horse. One very hard winter when many cattle died for want of forage, he went away from Hjardarholt to a place in the Breidafjord Dales which thereafter came to be known as Harrastadir and still is to this day. There he roamed about during the winter with sixteen other cattle and found grass for them all. In the spring he came back to his home pastures, to a place now called Harraból on the property of Hjardarholt. When Harri was eighteen years old, his "brunnvaka" fell off, and that same fall Óláf had him slaughtered. The very next night, a woman came to Óláf in a dream. She was big and fierce-looking and began to talk to him: "Are you asleep?" He said he was awake. She said "You are asleep, but it will amount to one and the same, sleeping or waking. You have had my son killed and caused him to come to me maimed and maltreated. Because of this you shall have to see your own son drenched in blood, and it shall be through my doing. I shall also pick out that one whose loss I know will be least easy to bear." After that she turned and vanished. Óláf woke up and thought he caught a glimpse of her. He took the dream very much to heart and told it to his friends, but it was never interpreted to his liking, so he preferred listening to those who said it was nothing but a silly dream that had passed before him.

32

Ósvíf and His Kin

THERE was a man called Ósvíf; he was the son of Helgi, who was the son of Óttar, who was the son of Bjorn the Eastman, who was the son of Ketil Flatnose, who was the son of Bjorn Buna. Ósvíf's mother was called Nidbjorg and her mother was Kadlín, a daughter of Gongu-Hrólf,[1] the son of Oxen-Thórir. Thórir was a famous *hersir* in Vík in eastern Norway. He was called Oxen-Thórir because he owned three islands with eighty oxen on each. He made King Hákon a present of one of the islands, together with the oxen on it, and this gift was much talked about.

Ósvíf was a very sage man. He lived at Laugar in Saelingsdal. The farm at Laugar stands south of the Saelingsdalsá opposite Tunga. Ósvíf's wife was Thórdís who was the daughter of Thjódólf the Short. One of their sons was called Óspak, another Helgi, a third Vandrád, a fourth Torrád, and a fifth Thórólf. They were all good fighting men. Gudrún was the name of their daughter. She was the fairest of all women born and raised in Iceland, foremost in beauty and intelligence. Gudrún was a woman of such courtly manner that in her day whatever other women had to boast of seemed but childish

CHART 14
THE LINEAGE OF KJARTAN AND GUDRUN

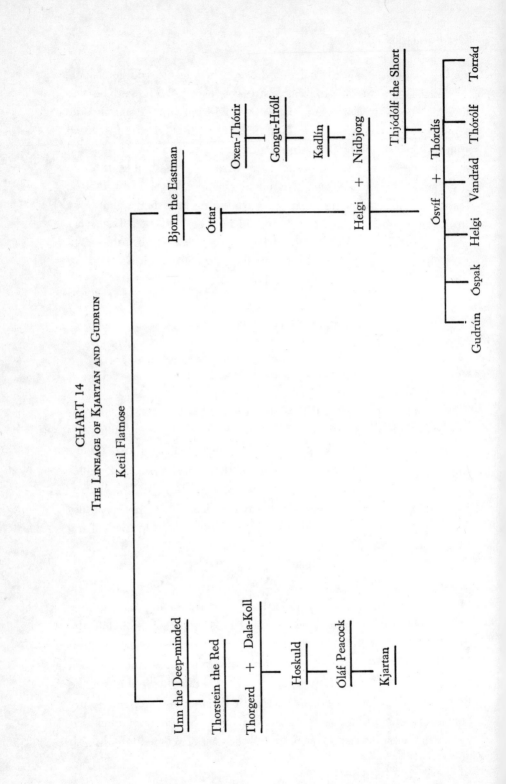

CHART 15

THE RELATIONS OF GUDRÚN'S SECOND HUSBAND THÓRD INGUNNARSON

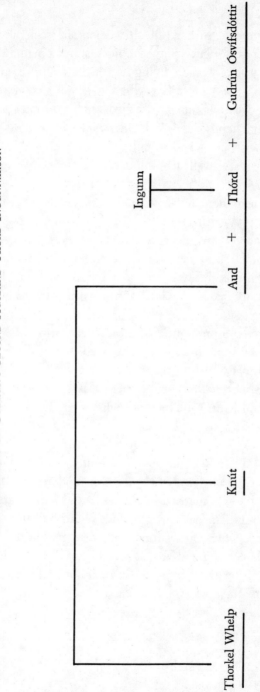

Thorkel Whelp   Knút   Aud   +   Thórd   +   Gudrún Ósvifsdóttir

Ingunn

trifles compared to her. Of all women she had the keenest wit and the cleverest tongue. She was liberal and openhanded.

There was a woman living at Ósvíf's by the name of Thórhalla, nicknamed the Chatterbox. She was some sort of relation to Ósvíf. She had two sons; one was called Odd, the other Stein. They were strong and handy men and did much of the hard work on Ósvíf's farm. They were given to talk and gossip just like their mother and were not very well liked, but Ósvíf's sons thought a great deal of them.

At Tunga there lived a man by the name of Thórarin, a son of Thórir the Wealthy.[2] He was an able farmer, a big man and strong. He had good lands but very little livestock. Ósvíf wanted to buy land from him because he, on the other hand, had much livestock and was short of land. So it came about that Ósvíf bought from Thórarin that part of his land which ran all the way from Gnúpuskord up along both sides of the valley as far as Stakkagil; these were good, fertile lands. So now he had a place to pasture his cattle. He always had a large household, and they lived very well.

West up at Saurbaer there is a farm called Hól. There two brothers lived together with their brother-in-law. The two brothers Thorkel Whelp and Knút were men of high birth. Their brother-in-law owned the farm with them. His name was Thórd. His mother's name was Ingunn and he was known by her and thus called Thórd Ingunnarson. Thórd's father's name was Glúm Geirason. Thórd was a handsome man, strong and sturdy, clever, and well versed in matters of the law. He was married to Thorkel's and Knút's sister Aud. She was neither beautiful nor capable, and Thórd had little love for her. He had married her mostly for her money, for the family had accumulated what amounted to a great fortune. Thorkel and Knút were doing well on their farm now that Thórd had come to have a hand in it with them.

CHART 16

Gudrún's Relationship to Gest and Thorgils Holluson

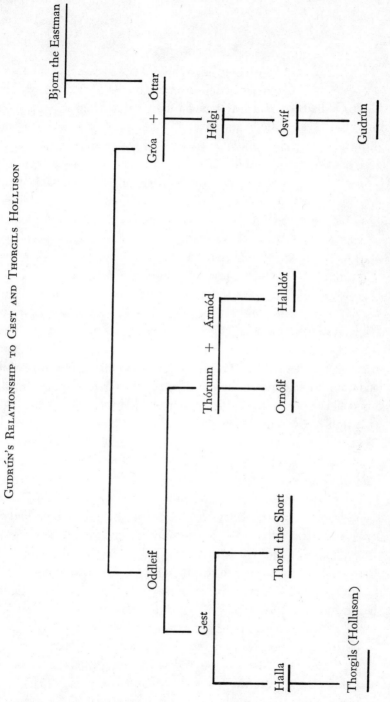

33

Two Rings and Two Headdresses

GEST Oddleifsson lived west in Bardastrond at Hagi. He was a great chieftain, keen-witted, and had the gift of second sight in many things. He was on friendly terms with all the more prominent people, and many sought out his counsel. He rode every summer to the Thing and always took his night lodging at Hól. So it happened one time that Gest rode to the Thing, as usual, and stayed overnight at Hól. He got himself ready early in the morning for he had a long way to go, as he planned on reaching his brother-in-law Ármód's place at Thykkvaskóg by nightfall. Ármód was married to Gest's sister Thórunn. Their sons were Ornólf and Halldór.

Now on that day Gest rode eastward out of Saurbaer and came to the hot spring at Laugar in Saelingsdal.[1] There he took a rest for a while. Gudrún came to the spring and gave her kinsman Gest a warm greeting, which he returned, and they fell to talking. Both of them were keen-witted and liked to visit. When the day was wearing on, Gudrún said: "I wish you would ride over to our farm this evening, kinsman, you and all your party. That is also my father's wish, although he gave me the honor of taking care of this errand for him. He also told me to tell you that he would like you to stay here whenever you ride to or from the west." Gest thanked her kindly and said this was indeed a very generous invitation, but he would have to ride on all the same as he had planned.

Gudrún then said: "I have had many dreams this winter, and there are four in particular which disturb me greatly. No one has been able to explain them to my satisfaction, and that is not because I insist that they be interpreted to my liking." "Tell me your dreams," said Gest; "it may be that we can make something of them." Gudrún began to relate: "I seemed to be standing outside by some brook, and I had a headdress on my head, but I found it ill-fitting, and I wanted to change it. There were many who said I should not do so. But I didn't listen to what they said and jerked the headdress off my head and threw it out into the brook, and that was the end of the dream."

And Gudrún continued: "At the beginning of the second dream I seemed to be standing by some lake, and somehow a silver bracelet had come on my arm. I seemed to own it, and thought it suited me very well. It was a most precious thing, so I thought, and I had every intention of keeping it for a very long time. But when I least expected it, the arm ring slipped off and into the lake, and I never saw it again. This loss seemed to me far greater than I ever imagined would be the case, had I lost an expensive thing. Then I woke up." Gest merely said: "This is no less of a dream."

Gudrún went on: "This is the third dream I had. I seemed to have a gold bracelet on, and it seemed to be my very own and to make up for my former loss. The thought entered my mind that I would get to enjoy this arm ring longer than I had the other, but it didn't seem as though this costly bracelet suited me that much better, it being gold instead of silver. Then I seemed to stumble and wanted to catch myself with my hand, but the gold bracelet struck against some stone and broke in two, and blood seemed to ooze from the pieces. What I felt then seemed to me more like grief than loss, and it occurred to me that there had been a slight crack in the bracelet and when I looked at the pieces afterwards, then I seemed to see many flaws in them. But yet I had the feeling that it might have remained whole, had I guarded it better. And that was the end of the dream." Gest merely said: "Your dreams are not on the wane."

And Gudrún went on: "My fourth dream was that I seemed to have a helmet on my head, which was made of gold and set with gems. I seemed to own this valuable thing. The chief fault with it, however, was that it was somewhat too heavy, for I could scarcely manage it and had to carry my head to one side. But in spite of this I didn't lay the blame on the helmet and had no intention of parting with it. All the same it toppled from my head and out into the Hvammsfjord. And after that I woke up. Now you have been told all the dreams."

Gest answered: "It's plain to me what these dreams mean. To you it will seem all very much of a piece, for I am going to interpret all of them in very much the same way. You will have four husbands, and I daresay when you get married to the first one, it won't be out of deep love. Where you seemed to have a large headdress on and it seemed so ill-fitting, that means you will have little love for him.

And where you took the headdress off and threw it into the water, that means you will leave him. That's what people call 'thrown to the winds,'[2] when a person throws away what he owns and gets nothing in return."

And Gest went on to say: "Then there was your second dream, in which you seemed to be wearing a silver bracelet. This means you will be married to a second man, one of fine and noble qualities. That one you will love much but get to enjoy for only a short time. I wouldn't be at all surprised if you lost him by drowning. I would not make any more of this dream."

"Then there was the third dream of yours, where you thought you had a gold bracelet on. That means that you will have a third husband; this one will not be that much dearer to you, as the one metal is rarer and dearer than the other. And if I don't miss my guess, about that time a change in faith will have taken place, and this husband of yours will have accepted the new faith, which we will deem by far the more exalted one. And where you thought the ring broke in two, somewhat due to your own carelessness, and saw blood ooze from the pieces, that means that your third husband will be slain, and it is then that you will see most clearly the flaws which existed in this marriage."

And Gest continued: "The fourth dream of yours was that you seemed to have a helmet on your head that was made of gold and set with precious stones. But it got too heavy for you to bear. That means you will have a fourth husband. He will be a great chieftain and will be overbearing and hold a helmet of terror[3] over you. And where it seemed to you that it tumbled into the Hvammsfjord, that means he will meet up with that same fjord on the very last day of his life. I cannot make any more out of this dream."

Gudrún's cheeks turned scarlet while the dreams were being interpreted, and she had not a word to say about it until Gest had done speaking. Then she said: "You might have foreseen fairer prophecies if the dreams I told you had warranted such. But I thank you all the same for having interpreted them. There certainly is much to look forward to if all of this is to come to pass."

Gudrún then asked Gest again to stay overnight with them, and said he and Ósvíf would have many worthwhile things to talk over with one another. "I must ride on," said Gest, "as I have said I would. But you must give your father my greetings and tell him that the time will come when there will be a shorter distance between our two dwellings than there is now, and then we will be able to talk to one another to our heart's content, if at that time we can talk to one another at all." After that Gudrún went home, and Gest rode away.

On his way he met a servant of Óláf's at the fence of Óláf's home meadow. The servant brought a message from Óláf asking Gest to Hjardarholt. Gest said he would visit Óláf in the course of the day but would spend the night at Thykkvaskóg. The servant turned back for home at once and told Óláf. So Óláf had horses brought and he rode out to meet Gest with some men. They caught up with Gest at the Ljá. Óláf bade him welcome and invited him to come to his farmstead together with all his party. Gest thanked him and said he would ride up to the farmstead to see his house, but would stay overnight with Ármód. Gest stayed a little while, yet made a thorough inspection of the farm and voiced his approval of everything, remarking that no money had been spared on that farm. Óláf rode along with Gest down to the Laxá.

During that day, Óláf's sons and Bolli, their foster brother, had been out swimming. Óláf's sons usually took the lead in this sport. There were also many young people from other farms out swimming. Kjartan and Bolli were just coming out of the water when the group came riding up. They were almost dressed by the time Gest and Óláf got there. Gest watched these young men for a while and then told Óláf where Kjartan was sitting and where Bolli. And then Gest pointed out Óláf's sons one by one with the shaft of his spear and named all of them that were there, and there were many other fine-looking young lads there too who had come from their swimming and were sitting on the river bank along with Kjartan and his brothers. Gest said he could not see any family resemblance to Óláf in these youths. Then Óláf said: "There is no overrating your keenness, Gest, when you can pick out and name people whom you've never seen before. But now I want you to tell me which one of these young men is likely to make the most of himself." Gest answered: "That will be in keeping with your fondest hopes that Kjartan be most highly esteemed as long as he lives."

Then Gest gave his horse the spur and rode away. A little later his son Thórd the Short rode up and fell in alongside and said: "What causes you to shed tears, father?" Gest replied: "It will do no good to say it, but I cannot be silent about what is certain to come to pass in your own day. It will be no surprise to me, if some day Bolli stands over Kjartan's crown and thereby also reaps his own death. An ill thing it is, to know this about such fine and sterling men." They rode on to the Thing and there all was quiet.

34

A Shirt for Thorvald

THERE was a man called Thorvald, the son of Halldór Garpsdalsgodi. He lived in Garpsdal on the Gilsfjord and was a wealthy man, but scarcely what one would call courageous. He asked Gudrún Ósvífs-dóttir in marriage at the Althing when she was fifteen years old. This proposal was not taken coldly, but Ósvíf said it would be plain from the terms of the marriage contract that he was not of equal standing with Gudrún. Thorvald answered in a mild manner, saying it was a wife he was asking for, not money. So Gudrún was betrothed to Thorvald, and Ósvíf set the terms, whereby it was decided that Gudrún alone should have control over their joint property as soon as they came into one bed, and she was to own half of it outright whether their married life were for longer or shorter. Furthermore, Thorvald was to buy jewels and costly things for Gudrún, such that no woman equally well-to-do could boast anything better, yet he was supposed to keep up his farm for all this buying. The people then rode home from the Thing.

Gudrún's consent had not been asked of this, and she openly showed her displeasure over it, but there the matter stood. The wedding feast was at Garpsdal in the double month.[1]

Gudrún showed little love for Thorvald and was hard to please when it came to buying finery. There was no trinket in all the Westfjords so dear that Gudrún did not think she ought to have it, and she paid Thorvald back with an ill temper if he did not buy it, no matter how costly it was. Thórd Ingunnarson got in thick with Thorvald and Gudrún and spent much of his time with them, and people often hinted at a love affair between Gudrún and Thórd.

One time when Gudrún asked Thorvald to buy some ornament for her, Thorvald said she knew no bounds and gave her a slap on the face. Then Gudrún said: "Now you have given me something we womenfolk take great pride in — rosy cheeks. And you have also put an end to my importuning you for things."

That same evening Thórd came over. Gudrún told him about the shameful treatment she had received and asked him how she could get back at Thorvald. Thórd smiled and said: "For this I have good advice. Make him a shirt with a wide neck opening and then declare yourself divorced from him."[2] Gudrún had no objection to this and no more was said. Gudrún declared herself divorced from Thorvald that very same spring and went home to Laugar. After that a settlement of Thorvald's and Gudrún's property was made, and she got half of all the wealth; and by that time her half share amounted to more than before. They had lived together for two years.

That same spring Ingunn sold her land at Króksfjord; the farm there was called Ingunnarstadir, the name it has had ever since. She moved west to Skálmarnes. She had been married to Glúm Geirason, as was written before. At that time Hallstein Godi lived at Hallsteinsnes west of Thorskafjord. He was an important and powerful man, but only moderately popular.

35

Mischief Afoot: The Kotkel Tribe

THERE was a man named Kotkel who had come out to Iceland not long before. His wife's name was Gríma. Their sons were Hallbjorn Sleek-stone Eye and Stígandi. These people came from the Hebrides. All of them were very skilled in magic and were great sorcerers. Hallstein Godi had taken them in, and they had settled down at Urdir in Skálmarfjord. Their settling there was none too well liked.

That summer Gest went to the Thing, going by ship to Saurbaer and staying overnight at Hól as was his wont. The brothers-in-law lent him horses as usual. Thórd Ingunnarson was along in Gest's party and stopped at Laugar in Saelingsdal. Gudrún Ósvífsdóttir rode to the Thing too, and Thórd Ingunnarson kept her company. Then one day as they were riding over the moorland of the Bláskógaheidi — a fine day it was—Gudrún remarked: "Is it true, Thórd, that your wife Aud always goes around in breeches with a seat gore in them and swathings wrapped around her legs all the way down to her shoes?" He said he had not noticed that. "It can't be very important then, if you haven't noticed it. But why then is she called Breeches Aud?" Thórd said: "I don't imagine she has been called that for very long." Gudrún answered: "What's going to mean more to her is that this name will be hers for a long time to come." And so everybody arrived at the Thing, where nothing to speak of happened.

Thórd spent a great deal of his time in Gest's booth and was always talking to Gudrún. One day Thórd Ingunnarson asked Gudrún what the penalty was for a woman who always wore breeches like the menfolk. Gudrún answered: "The same penalty applies in that case to a woman as to a man who wears a shirt with a neck opening so large that his nipples show — in both cases grounds for divorce." Then Thórd said: "What would you advise? That I declare myself divorced from Aud here at the Thing? Or in my home district where I could get the backing of more men? For those who will feel wronged by this are powerful and proud-minded men." Gudrún reflected for a moment and then said: "The sluggard's business bides the evening." Thórd jumped right to his feet and went straight to the Law Rock, named his witnesses and declared himself divorced from Aud, giving as grounds that she wore breeches with a seat gore just like the menfolk.

Aud's brothers took it ill, but nonetheless everything stayed quiet. Thórd rode away from the Thing with Ósvíf's sons. But when Aud heard this news, she said:

> Well it is I wot,
> Whence forsaken and alone.[1]

Thereafter Thórd rode west to Saurbaer in a party of twelve for the settlement of the property, and that went off smoothly, for Thórd was not particular as to how it was divided. Thórd drove many head of cattle from the west to Laugar. After that he asked for Gudrún's hand and easily got Ósvíf's consent, and Gudrún raised no objections. The wedding was to be at Laugar when there were still ten weeks of summer. This feast was a most splendid one.

Thórd's and Gudrún's married life went well. Thorkel Whelp and Knút did not take up proceedings against Thórd Ingunnarson for the simple reason that they got no backing for it.

The next summer the folk from Hól went up into Hvammsdal with their cattle for summer pasturage. Aud was up there at the shiel[2] too. The Laugar folk had their summer shiel up in Lambadal, which cuts westward into the mountains from Saelingsdal. Aud asked the cowhand how often he chanced to meet the herder from Laugar. He said it naturally happened all the time since the two shielings were only separated by a ridge. Aud then said, "Today you are to make a point of seeing the herder from Laugar so that you can find out for me which of the men are down at the farm and which ones at the summer quarters. Speak by all means kindly of Thórd, as is only right." The boy promised to do as she asked.

When the herder came back home in the evening, Aud asked what he had learned. The herder answered: "I have good news for you. The floor space between Thórd's and Gudrún's bedclosets has widened, for she is at the summer hut and he is working himself to death building a sleeping hall, and he and Ósvíf are alone down at the winter quarters." "You have done a good job of sounding things out," said Aud. "Have two horses saddled and ready when the men go to bed."

The shepherd boy did as she ordered; and a little while before sunset, Aud mounted her horse, and this was one time she had breeches on and no mistake. The shepherd boy rode the other horse and could scarcely keep up with her, so hard and fast did she spur her horse on. She rode south across the moors of the Saelingsdalsheidi and did not stop until she came to the home meadow at Laugar. Then she dismounted and asked the shepherd boy to tend the horses while she went to the house. Aud walked up to the door and found it open; she went into the fire-hall and over to the bedcloset where Thórd was lying fast asleep. The bedcloset door was pulled to, but the bolt was not fastened. She went in and found him sleeping face

up. Aud woke him, and he turned over on his side when he saw
that a man had come in. She drew a stubby sword and lunged at
Thórd with it, dealing him a heavy wound. The cut went across his
right hand and breast nipples. She followed the stroke through with
such force that the sword came to rest in the bolster. Then Aud left
and went back to her horse, mounted, and rode home.

Thórd tried to spring to his feet after he received the blow, but
could not, for he was weakened by loss of blood. Ósvíf woke up at this
and asked what had happened. Thórd said he had got badly hurt
somehow. Ósvíf asked if he knew who had done it to him and got up
and bound his wound. Thórd said he guessed Aud had done it. Ósvíf
offered to ride after her, saying that she probably had come out there
with but few men, and punishment would serve her right. Thórd
would not hear of it, saying she had only done what she had to.

Aud got home about sunrise and her brothers asked her where she
had been. Aud said she had gone to Laugar and told them what had
befallen on her trip. They voiced their approval of it and said the
only trouble was that she had not done nearly enough. Thórd lay a
long time with his wounds. His chest healed together well, but his
hand never mended completely so that he could grip as well with it
as before. All was quiet that winter.

The following spring, Ingunn, Thórd's mother, came east from
Skálmarnes. Thórd bade her welcome. She said she wanted his protection and aid, explaining that Kotkel and his wife and sons were
giving her trouble with their thievery and witchcraft and that they
were getting much support from Hallstein Godi. Thórd took the
matter up at once and said he would straighten things out with those
thieves even if Hallstein were against him. He started out immediately, ten men in all, and Ingunn too went west with him. He got a
ferry at Tjaldanes and sailed west to Skálmarnes. Thórd had all the
chattels which belonged to his mother put on board. The sheep and
cattle were to be driven inland along the fjords. Altogether there were
twelve on board — there was another woman besides Ingunn.

Then Thórd went to Kotkel's farm with his men. Kotkel's sons
were not at home. Thórd then raised his charges against Kotkel and
Gríma and their sons for theft and sorcery, saying that he would de-

mand outlawry as punishment and would summon the case before
the Althing.[3] After that he returned to his ship.

Hallbjorn and Stígandi came home just as Thórd had got a short
distance offshore. Kotkel then told his sons what had happened. The
brothers were infuriated at this and declared no one had ever before
come out against them in such open hostility. Thereupon Kotkel had
a big incantation scaffold built. They all climbed up on it and chanted
powerfully wrought charms; these were magic spells. Presently a violent storm broke loose.

Thórd Ingunnarson and his companions felt the effects of this out
at sea where they were, for it was precisely against them that the
storm was set. The ship was driven westward out beyond Skálmarnes. Thórd showed great courage and seamanship. People who
were on shore saw him throw everything overboard that added to
the weight — everything except the very men themselves. They had
hopes that Thórd would reach land safely, for he had by then passed
the place thickest with rocks and reefs. But then a breaker suddenly
rose up a little way from land, one which nobody remembered ever
having seen there before, and hit so hard against the ship that it
turned keel up all at once. There Thórd and all his company
drowned, and the ship was dashed to splinters. The keel drifted
ashore to a place which ever since has had the name Kjalarey (Keel
Isle). Thórd's shield washed up on an island which was called
Skjaldarey (Shield Isle) ever after. The bodies of Thórd and his
companions also soon washed ashore. There a mound was cast up
over them and that place has been called Haugsnes (Mound's Ness)
ever since.

36

A Prize Stud of Horses

These tidings spread far and wide and were ill spoken of. People
who carried on such witchcraft as Kotkel and his family were thought
deserving of no less than death. Gudrún felt Thórd's loss very deeply;
she was also with child and her time was near. She gave birth to a
boy, and he was sprinkled with water and given the name Thórd.

At that time Snorri Godi was living at Helgafell; he was a kinsman and friend of Ósvíf's, and Gudrún and her family had a staunch supporter in him. Snorri was invited to Laugar for a feast; and when he came Gudrún told him her troubles. Snorri said he would give her his support whenever the right time presented itself. To comfort her in the meantime he offered to foster her son. Gudrún accepted this and said she would rely on his judgment. Gudrún's son Thórd was nicknamed the Cat. He was the father of Stúf the Scald.

After that Gest Oddleifsson went to see Hallstein Godi and gave him two choices: either he would have to drive these sorcerers away or they would be slain — "and it's too late as it is." Hallstein wasted no time in making his choice, and told Kotkel's family they had better be on their way and not settle any place west of the Dala- heidi moorland, adding that by rights they ought to be killed.

Then Kotkel and his family went off, taking with them no posses- sions other than four studhorses. The stallion was black, a large and handsome animal, and tried and true in horse fighting.[1] Nothing is told of their moves and whereabouts before they came to Kambsnes, to Thorleik Hoskuldsson's. Thorleik asked if he might purchase the horses from them, for he could see that they were valuable animals. Kotkel answered: "I will make a bargain with you on this. You take the horses and in return give me some place to live hereabouts in your vicinity." Thorleik said: "Won't the horses come to cost me rather dearly then? I've heard tell that you have quite a few enemies in this district." Kotkel answered: "You no doubt mean the Laugar folk." Thorleik said that was so. Then Kotkel said: "But the story of our dealings with Gudrún and her brothers may look quite a bit different from what you have been told. There has been no call for people to hurl such slander against us. You may as well take the horses, as far as that goes. From what we've heard about you, we will not be put at the mercy of people in this district if we have your support."

Thorleik now decided to strike the bargain, for the horses did look tempting and Kotkel pleaded his case shrewdly. So Thorleik took the horses and found Kotkel and his family a place to live at Leidólfs- stadir in Laxárdal. He also provided them with livestock.

The Laugar folk learned of this, and Ósvíf's sons wanted to set out against Kotkel and his sons at once. But Ósvíf told them: "Let us take Snorri Godi's advice and leave this job to others. For it won't be long before Kotkel's neighbors have brand new charges against them, and Thorleik will have to bear the brunt of it, and that'll serve him right. And it won't be long before many turn his enemy, whose esteem he strove long to gain. But if others haven't already driven them out of the district or killed them outright by the time three years have passed, then I'll not stand in the way of your doing whatever you see fit with this Kotkel tribe." To this Gudrún and her brothers agreed.

Kotkel and his family scarcely did any work to support themselves, but for all that they stood in no need of buying either hay or food throughout the winter. Their settling there was none too well liked, but no one dared harm them for fear of Thorleik.

37

An Ill-paid Favor

ONE SUMMER at the Thing when Thorleik was sitting in his booth, a big man happened by. He greeted Thorleik, who returned the greeting and asked him his name and where he came from. He said his name was Eldgrím and that he lived at Borgarfjord on the farm called Eldgrímsstadir. This farm is in the valley which cuts west into the mountains between Múli and Grísartunga. It is now called Grímsdal. Thorleik said: "I've heard tell that you're no petty person to deal with." Eldgrím said: "I came because I want to buy those fine studhorses you got from Kotkel last summer." Thorleik answered: "The horses are not for sale." Eldgrím replied: "I'll offer you equally as many horses in return and even something more into the bargain. Many will say I'm offering you twice as much as they are worth." Thorleik answered: "I'm no tradesmonger. You'll never get those horses, even if you offer me three times their worth." Eldgrím retorted: "It's no lie that you are proud and stubborn. I'd just like to see you offered a worse price and have to part with the horses anyway." Thorleik turned very red at these words and said: "You'll have

to come to much closer quarters with me, Eldgrím, if you are going
to bully me out of the horses." Eldgrím said: "You seem to think it
unlikely that you'll ever get worsted by me, but I'm going to come
and take a look at the horses this summer, and then we'll see which
of us owns them from then on." Thorleik said: "Go ahead and hold
to your promise, but don't deal me any unfair odds." That was the end
of their talk. Those who had overheard this said that each of them
had got what was coming to him. After that the people went home
from the Thing, and nothing else happened to speak of.

Early one morning one of the men was making his rounds there at
Hrútsstadir, Hrút Herjólfsson's place. When he came in, Hrút asked
him if he had anything to report. He said he had no news except
that he had seen a man riding over beyond the shallows up to where
Thorleik's horses were— "and this man dismounted and was capturing
the horses." Hrút asked just where the horses had been. The housecarl said: "They were keeping well to their pasture, grazing as usual
in your meadow down below the fence wall." Hrút answered: "It's
true all right that our kinsman Thorleik isn't too particular about
boundaries when it comes to pasturage. So it seems hardly likely
that he has ordered the horses to be driven away." Hrút jumped up in
undershirt and linen breeches, threw on a grey cloak, and grabbed
the gold-inlaid halberd which King Harald had given him. He was
in no little hurry when he went out, and there he saw the man driving the horses on down below the fence. Hrút struck out in that direction and saw that it was Eldgrím who was driving the horses off.
Hrút hailed him, and Eldgrím returned the greeting, though not very
readily. Hrút asked where he thought he was going with the horses.
Eldgrím answered: "I'll not hide it from you, although I know you
and Thorleik are related. I have come after his horses, and he'll never
see them again if I have my way. Besides I have done just as I promised him at the Thing and have not come after them with a whole
band of men."

Hrút said: "That's not what I call courage if you take the horses
away while Thorleik is fast asleep in his bed. You would best live up
to your agreement with him if you'd make a point of seeing him
before you ride out of the district with his horses." Eldgrím said:
"Give Thorleik warning if you want to, for you can see that I have

come from home prepared. It would suit me fine, if Thorleik and I
happened upon one another." And with that he brandished the
barbed spear which he had in his hand. He also had on a helmet,
carried a sword, had a shield at his side, and wore a coat of mail.
Hrút spoke: "I'd rather try something else instead of running all the
way over to Kambsnes, for I am heavy of foot. But Thorleik is not
going to be robbed if I can help it, even though we don't make much
of our kinship." Eldgrím said: "You don't mean to say you intend
to snatch the horses away from me?" Hrút answered: "I'll give you
another stud of horses if you'll let these loose, although mine may
not be quite as good as these." Eldgrím said: "It's all very fine and
good what you say, Hrút, but now that I've got my hands on Thorleik's horses, no bribes or threats of yours are going to wrest them
from me." Then Hrút answered: "I think you're making a choice
which will prove the worse for both of us."

At that point Eldgrím wanted to put an end to this talk and gave
his horse the spur. But when Hrút saw that, he raised up his halberd
and flung it between Eldgrím's shoulders so that the coat of mail split
right apart and the halberd flew out through his chest. Eldgrím fell
off his horse dead, needless to say. Then Hrút buried him and that
place is now called Eldgrímsholt and is south of Kambsnes. After
that Hrút rode down to Kambsnes and told Thorleik the news.
Thorleik flew into a rage and seemed to feel Hrút's action had put
him in disgrace, whereas Hrút thought he had done him a great
favor. Thorleik said two things were certain — something ill had
prompted him to do it and nothing good would come of it in return.
Hrút said that would depend entirely on Thorleik. They parted on
no friendly terms.

Hrút was eighty years old when he killed Eldgrím, and it was
generally thought that he had gained in honor from this deed. But
the fact that Hrút had grown in the sight of others by this deed made
him none the greater in Thorleik's eyes. To his mind it was obvious
that he himself would have won out over Eldgrím, had they been
allowed to meet up with one another, seeing how little favored by
fortune Eldgrím was. Now Thorleik went to see his tenants Kotkel
and Gríma and asked them to do something which would put Hrút
to shame. They took this up eagerly and said they were willing to do

so. Then Thorleik went home. A little later Kotkel, Gríma, and their sons started out from home by night. They went to Hrút's farm and worked a great magic spell there. When the sounds of the incantation first began, those inside the house did not quite know what to make of it. The chanting, though, was sweet to listen to. Hrút was the only one who knew the meaning of these sounds and said no one should look out that night — "and everyone who can, keep awake; if you do as I say, no harm will come to us." But all the same they all fell asleep. Hrút stayed awake the longest, but at last he too dozed off.

Hrút had a son, Kári, who then was twelve years old and the most promising of Hrút's children, and Hrút loved him very much. Kári scarcely fell asleep at all, for it was against him that the spell was cast. He felt very restless and jumped up and looked out. He walked out toward the place where they were holding the incantations and at once fell down dead.

When the household woke up in the morning, Hrút missed Kári. A little way from the door he was found dead. Hrút felt this as the greatest loss and he had a mound raised up over Kári. Afterwards he rode to Óláf Hoskuldsson and told him what had befallen. Óláf was infuriated over this and said it had been a great lack of forethought on their part to let such evil people as Kotkel and his family live so close by, and also admitted that Thorleik had dealt himself an ill share in this affair with Hrút, but added that more had probably come of it than he, Thorleik, had intended. Óláf said Kotkel, his wife and sons should be put to death at once — "and it's too late now as it is."

Óláf and Hrút set out with fifteen men. When Kotkel and his people saw a group of men riding up to their farm, they all took to their heels for the mountain. There Hallbjorn Sleek-stone Eye was caught, and a skin bag was drawn over his head. Men were left to watch over him while the others searched for Kotkel, Gríma, and Stígandi up on the mountain. Kotkel and Gríma were captured on the ridge between Haukadal and Laxárdal. There they were stoned to death, and a cairn was made for them out of the stones. Even to this day one can see traces of it, and the place is called Skrattavardi (Sor-

cerers' Cairn). Stígandi made his way down from the ridge south
into Haukadal, and there was lost from sight.

Hrút and his sons went down to the sea with Hallbjorn, put out
a boat, and rowed out from land with him. Then they took the skin
bag off his head and tied a stone around his neck. Hallbjorn turned
his gaze toward shore, and his look was anything but good.[1] Then
Hallbjorn said: "That was an unlucky day for us when we kinsmen
came to Kambsnes and met up with Thorleik. May he enjoy but few
pleasant days there from this day forth, and may life be made difficult
for anyone who settles there in his place." This curse seems very much
to have taken effect. After that they drowned him and rowed back
to land.

Not long after that, Hrút went to see his kinsman Óláf and told
him that he would not have matters stand as they were with Thorleik
and asked Óláf to get him some men to make an attack on him. But
Óláf answered: "It isn't right for you kinsmen to be laying hands on
one another. It has been an unfortunate turn of events for Thorleik.
Let's try rather for a peaceful settlement between you. You have often
shown that you can be long-suffering and wait for your just due."
Hrút said: "There's no point in trying that. It will never be mended
between us. I'd prefer that we two no longer live side by side in Laxárdal." Óláf answered: "You're not to take any steps against Thorleik,
more than I allow. And if you do, it is not unlikely that 'the valley
will meet a hill.'"[2] Hrút saw that he would get nowhere, so he went
home, most ill-content. Everything was quiet, so to speak, and everyone sat around peacefully the rest of that year.

38

The End of the Kotkel Tribe

BUT TO get back and tell of Stígandi. He became an outlaw and
difficult to cope with. There was a man by the name of Thórd who
lived in Hundadal. He was a wealthy man, but not of any great
account. A strange thing happened at Hundadal that summer — the
cows started giving but little milk. A woman was looking after the

cattle there. People began to notice that she was acquiring quite a few precious things and used to disappear for long periods at a time, so that nobody knew where she was. Thórd had her coerced into telling, and becoming frightened, she owned that a man had been coming to her. "He is big," she said, "and what I would call good-looking." Then Thórd asked how soon this man might come to see her again. She said she expected it would be soon.

After that Thórd went to have a talk with Óláf and told him that Stígandi was very likely somewhere in the vicinity, and asked Óláf to go with him together with his men to capture him. Óláf lost no time in acting and went to Hundadal. The bondwoman was then fetched and questioned. Óláf asked her where Stígandi might be hiding out. She said she did not know. Óláf then offered to reward her if she would give them a chance at Stígandi. They made an agreement between them.

That same day she went out as usual to look after her cows. And when Stígandi came to her, she welcomed him and offered to look in his hair for lice. He laid his head in her lap and soon fell fast asleep. After that she slipped out from under his head and went to find Óláf and his men and told them how things stood. They went to where Stígandi was lying, determined that Stígandi should not get the same chance as his brother had to bring evil down upon them with his glance. So they took a skin bag and pulled it down over his head. Stígandi awoke at this, but made no struggle, for now there were many against one. There was a slit in the skin bag, and Stígandi got a glimpse of the slope across the way. There the lay of the land was fair and covered with thick grass. But suddenly something like a whirlwind started up and stirred up the earth so that never did grass come up there again. This place is now called Brenna (Burnt Spot). Thereupon they stoned Stígandi to death and buried him under a heap of stones. Óláf made good his promise to the bond-woman and gave her her freedom, and she went home with him to Hjardarholt.

Hallbjorn Sleek-stone Eye was tossed up by the surf not long after he was drowned. That place is called Knarrarnes where they buried him. He walked again a great deal as a ghost.

There was a man named Thorkel the Bald. He lived at Thykkva-

skóg on property inherited from his father. He was a big and bold
fellow, and of great strength. One evening a cow was missing at
Thykkvaskóg, and Thorkel and his housecarl went out to look for her.
It was after sunset, but there was bright moonlight. Thorkel said that
one of them should go one way and one the other. And when Thorkel
was alone, he thought he saw a cow in the woods before him, but
when he got there it was Sleek-stone Eye and no cow. They started
to grapple with one another with all their might; Hallbjorn gave
ground and when Thorkel was least on his guard, he slipped out of
his grasp and down into the earth. After that Thorkel went home.
His servant had already got home and had found the cow. After that
no one suffered any more harm from Hallbjorn.

Thorbjorn Skrjúp was dead by this time and so was Melkorka. Both
of them lie in a cairn in Laxárdal. Their son Lambi lived on the
farm after them. He was a big and bold fellow and was very well-off.
Lambi was more highly thought of than his father had been, because
of his kinship on his mother's side. The kinsmen, Lambi and Óláf,
were on good terms with one another.

The winter following Kotkel's killing came to an end, and in the
spring the two brothers Óláf and Thorleik got together, and Óláf
asked Thorleik whether he intended to keep on with his farm. Thorleik said he did. Óláf said: "There is one thing I would like to ask of
you, kinsman, and that is that you break up your household and go
abroad. You will be considered a man of distinction wherever you
go, and as for our kinsman Hrút, I think he feels rather cool toward
you owing to what's happened in your dealings with one another. I
don't want to run the risk any longer of you two being such close
neighbors. Hrút is powerful, and his sons are overbearing and bold
fellows. I feel that I will be in a difficult position for kinship's sake,
should it come to real blows between the two of you, kinsmen of
mine as you both are." Thorleik said: "I have no qualms about not
being able to hold my own against Hrút and his sons, and I'll not
leave the country because of them. But if on the other hand you feel
it's so important, kinsman, and think you will be put in a difficult
position, then I will take you at your word and do it because you say
so. Besides, I felt most content with my lot when I was abroad. I
also know that you will not treat my son Bolli any the worse for my

not being anywhere near, for you know I love him more than anyone
else." Óláf answered: "In following my wish you have chosen the
right course. And as for Bolli, I have every intention of being to him
henceforth what I have been hitherto. I shall treat him no worse than
my own sons." After this the brothers parted in great friendship.

Thorleik sold his lands and used the money for the journey abroad.
He bought a ship which was drawn up at Dogurdarnes. When everything was ready, he and his wife and all his household went abroad.
The ship had a good voyage and made Norway in the fall. From
there Thorleik sailed south to Denmark, for he no longer felt at
home in Norway, his kinsmen and friends there being either dead or
driven out of the country. From there he held his course to Gotaland.[1]
It is generally said that Thorleik was spared having to contend with
old age, but nonetheless was much esteemed as long as he did live.
And here we come to the end of the story of Thorleik.

39

Laugar

THERE continued to be much talk round about the Breidafjord Dales
of Hrút's and Thorleik's quarrel, and how Hrút had suffered greatly
at the hands of Kotkel and his sons. When speaking of it to Gudrún
and her brothers, Ósvíf asked, if, in thinking back, they still thought
they should have laid themselves open to the risk of dealing with
such hellhounds as Kotkel and his lot. Gudrún said: "He who has
your counsel at his disposal is never at a loss, father."

Óláf now sat contentedly on his farm in high honor, and all his
sons were at home, as well as their kinsman and foster brother Bolli.
Kjartan was by far the foremost of Óláf's sons. He and Bolli loved
one another the most, and Kjartan could not go anywhere but that
Bolli went along.

Kjartan often went to the hot spring in Saelingsdal, and it always
happened that Gudrún was at the spring too. Kjartan liked visiting
with Gudrún, for she was quick-witted and had a clever tongue. It
was common talk that Kjartan and Gudrún would make the best

matched couple of all the young people then growing up. There was also great friendship between Óláf and Ósvíf, and they were always partying back and forth — not any the less so now that a fondness was developing between the young people.

One time when Óláf was talking to Kjartan he said: "I don't know why it always weighs so heavily on my mind when you go to Laugar and see Gudrún. It is not that I don't consider Gudrún far above all other women, for she alone is the one whom I deem an equal match for you. Something tells me — but I don't want to prophesy this — that we kinsmen and the folk over at Laugar may not be lucky in our dealings with one another, right up to the last." Kjartan said he did not want to go against his father's will if he could help it, but said he hoped this might take a better turn than was his guess. Kjartan continued his usual habit of going to Laugar, and Bolli always went with him. And so the seasons passed.

CHART 17
THE LINEAGE OF KALF AND HREFNA

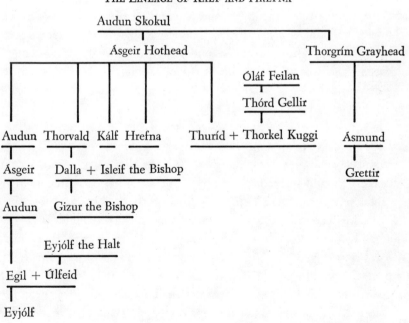

40

Kjartan and Bolli with King Óláf Tryggvason

THERE was a man named Ásgeir who was nicknamed Hothead. He lived at Ásgeirsá in Víðidal and was the son of Audun Skokul.[1] Ásgeir was the first of his kinsmen to come to Iceland, where he claimed land at Víðidal. Another son of Audun was called Thorgrím Grayhead. He was the father of Ásmund, who was the father of Grettir. Ásgeir Hothead had five children. One of his sons was called Audun, who was the father of Ásgeir, who was the father of Audun, who was the father of Egil who was married to Úlfeid, the daughter of Eyjólf the Halt. Their son was Eyjólf, who was killed at the Althing. A second son of Ásgeir Hothead's was called Thorvald. He had a daughter Dalla, who was married to Bishop Ísleif.[2] Their son was Bishop Gizur. A third son of Ásgeir's was called Kálf. All of Ásgeir's sons showed great promise. Kálf Ásgeirsson was at that time out traveling and trading abroad and was thought a most capable man. A daughter of Ásgeir's was called Thuríd, and she was married to Thorkel Kuggi, Thórd Gellir's son. Their son was Thorstein. A second daughter of Ásgeir's was called Hrefna. She was the most beautiful of women there in the north country and had many admirers. Ásgeir was a prominent and able man.

One time Kjartan Óláfsson set out south for Borgarfjord. Nothing is told of his trip until he came to Borg. There Thorstein Egilsson, his mother's brother, was living at the time. Bolli was with him on the trip, for the foster brothers were such good friends that neither seemed to be happy or enjoy anything if the other was not along. Thorstein received Kjartan in all friendliness and said that the longer Kjartan stayed there the better, as far as he was concerned. So Kjartan stayed at Borg for quite a while. There was a ship lying up at the mouth of the Gufuá that summer. It belonged to Kálf Ásgeirsson, who had been staying with Thorstein Egilsson over the winter. Kjartan told Thorstein privately that his real reason for coming south was to buy half interest in the ship from Kálf. "For I have in mind to travel abroad," he said, and asked Thorstein what he thought of Kálf. Thorstein said he thought Kálf was a fine fellow. "It is very understandable, kinsman," said Thorstein, "that you desire to learn about the ways of other people. Your journey is sure to be remarkable in some way or other, and there is much at stake for your kinsmen in how it will turn out for you." Kjartan said he was sure it would turn out well.

Then Kjartan bought half interest in the ship from Kálf, and they formed a partnership with equal shares. Kjartan was to come to the ship after ten weeks of summer had passed. Upon leaving Borg, Kjartan was sent off with gifts, and he and Bolli then rode home. When Óláf heard about this new venture, he felt Kjartan had made a hasty decision, but nevertheless said he would not try to change things.

A little while thereafter Kjartan rode to Laugar and told Gudrún about his going abroad. "You have made a rather hasty decision, Kjartan," Gudrún said, and she added a few words from which Kjartan could gather that she felt displeased about it. Kjartan said: "Don't be annoyed over this. I shall do something else to make it right with you." Gudrún answered: "Hold to your promise, for I can tell you now what I want." Kjartan asked her to do so. Gudrún said: "It is this: I want to go abroad with you this summer. Then you will more than have made up for your rash decision, for I don't like it here in Iceland." "That cannot be," said Kjartan; "your brothers are still young and inexperienced, and your father is old. If you leave the country, they will be without anyone to look after them. But wait for me for three years." Gudrún said she would make no such promise, and each would only see it his way. With that they parted and Kjartan rode home.

In summer Óláf rode to the Thing, and Kjartan rode east with his father from Hjardarholt. They parted company at Nordrárdal and from there Kjartan rode to the ship, with Bolli, his kinsman. There were ten Icelanders in all who accompanied Kjartan on his way, and all were loath to part from him, so fond were they of him. So Kjartan rode on to the ship with this company of friends.

There Kálf Ásgeirsson welcomed them. Kjartan and Bolli had brought many wares with them. They now worked at getting them- selves ready, and as soon as a breeze came up, they sailed out along the Borgarfjord with a light but good wind, and then out to sea. They had good sailing and made Norway to the north at Trondheim. They landed at Agdanes and found some men there to talk to and asked for news. They were told that there had been a change of rulers in the land. Earl Hákon was dead and King Óláf Tryggvason had succeeded him, and all Norway had fallen under his sway. King Óláf was ordering a change of faith in Norway, and people were divided in their stand on this matter. Kjartan and his party laid their ship in at Nidarós.

At that time there were many Icelanders in Norway who were prominent men. There were three ships moored at the landing stage, all of them owned by Icelanders. Brand the Generous, the son of Vermund Thorgrímsson, owned one of them, Hallfred the Difficult Scald[3] the second, and the third belonged to two brothers, one called Bjarni and the other Thórhall. They were the sons of Skeggi from Breidá out east in Fljótshlíd.[4] All these men had intended to sail out to Iceland that summer, but the king had put a ban on their ships because they did not want to accept the new faith he was proclaiming.

Kjartan was welcomed by all the Icelanders, and most of all by Brand, for he and Kjartan had known each other before. The Icelanders now took counsel with one another and agreed to reject the new faith which the king decreed, and all those just mentioned swore to stick by one another. Kjartan and his mates now put their ship up to the landing stage, unloaded it, and made arrangements for their goods.

King Óláf was in town and heard about the ship's arrival and also that there were many on board who were prominent men. One fine day in fall it happened that people went out from the town to swim in the river Nid. Kjartan and his party saw this, and Kjartan told his companions they might go swimming too to amuse themselves that day, so they did. There was one man there who was by far the best swimmer of them all. Kjartan asked Bolli if he wanted to attempt a swimming match against this townsman. Bolli replied: "I don't think I would have a chance." "I don't know what has become of your competitive spirit," Kjartan said, "but if you won't, I will." Bolli answered: "You can if you like."

Kjartan now dives out into the river and swims toward the man who is the best swimmer, and ducks him down under the water and holds him down for a while. Then Kjartan lets him come up. But they were not up long, when the man suddenly takes hold of Kjartan and pushes him under, and they stay down none too short a time to suit Kjartan. Then they come up again. Not a word did either have to say to the other. A third time they go down, and this time they remain under by far the longest. And now Kjartan begins to have his doubts about how this sport will end and cannot ever recall having been in such a tight spot before. Then at last they come up and swim for land.

Then the townsman asked: "Who might this man be?" Kjartan told him his name. The townsman said: "You are a good swimmer. Are you as good at other sports as at this?" Kjartan answered, though not very readily: "So it was said while I was in Iceland, that the others followed suit, but now that doesn't mean much." The townsman said: "That all depends on with whom you have competed. But why don't you ask *me* anything?" Kjartan said: "Because I don't care who you are." The townsman said: "Two things are certain — you are an accomplished fellow, but also puffed-up. All the same you shall get to know my name and who it is you have been swimming with. Here before you is Óláf Tryggvason, the king."

Kjartan had nothing to say and turned away at once. He was dressed in a kirtle of red scarlet, but was without a cloak. The king was nearly dressed by then and called to Kjartan, telling him not to be in such a hurry. Kjartan turned around, though not very readily. Then the king took his own cloak off his shoulders and gave it to Kjartan, saying he should not go back to his men cloakless. Kjartan thanked the king for the gift and went to his men and showed them the cloak. They voiced anything but approval of this and thought Kjartan had put himself too much under the king's power. Then things were quiet.

Bad weather set in that fall with much frost and cold. The heathen people maintained that it was not at all to be wondered at that the weather turned bad — "It's because of the king's new-fangled ideas and this new faith that the gods are angry." The Icelanders all stayed together in the town during the winter, and it was Kjartan who took the leadership among them. The weather got better, and a great

crowd of people came to town at the summons of King Óláf. Many
people in Trondheim had accepted the Christian faith, but nonetheless those numbered many more who held out against it. One day
the king called together a Thing in town out at Eyrar by the Nid
and preached the faith to the people, both at length and eloquently.
The Trondheimers had a host of men present, and they in turn
offered battle to the king. The king said they should bear in mind
that he had had far greater forces to contend with than just fighting
cotters in Trondheim. At that the farmers were panic-stricken and
gave themselves over into the king's power. Many people were then
baptized, and after that the Thing came to an end.

That same evening the king sent some men to the quarters of the
Icelanders to find out what they were talking about. They went and
did so. A great din was to be heard inside. Then Kjartan spoke up
and said to Bolli: "How keen are you, kinsman, on accepting this
faith which the king is proclaiming?" "I'm not at all keen on it,"
answered Bolli, "for this faith of theirs seems pithless to me." Kjartan asked: "Didn't you have the feeling that the king held out threats
against those reluctant to submit to his will?" Bolli answered: "To
my mind the king didn't leave a shadow of a doubt that they could
expect hard treatment at his hands." "No one is going to get me
under his thumb," said Kjartan, "not as long as I can stand on my
own two feet and wield a weapon. To my mind it's unmanly to be
taken like a sheep out of the fold or a fox out of a trap. If one has to
die in any case, my choice would be to do something beforehand
which people would talk about for a long time to come." Bolli asked:
"What do you intend to do?" "I'll make no secret of it," said Kjartan,
"burn the king inside his hall." "There's nothing unmanly about
that, I'd say," answered Bolli, "but I don't see how it can ever be
done. Good luck and a mighty guardian spirit[5] seem to be at the
king's side. He also has a reliable guard keeping watch day and
night." Kjartan said that was the trouble with most — courage failed
them in the end, be they ever such good men otherwise. Bolli said
it would remain to be seen who needed to challenge whose courage.
The others chimed in that this was useless talk. After the king's men
had learned this, they left and reported everything back to the king.

The following morning the king called together a Thing. This time the Icelanders received a summons to it. When the Thing was brought to order, the king got up and thanked the people for coming there — all those who wanted to be his friends and had accepted the new faith. The Icelanders were called up for a parley. The king asked whether they wanted to be baptized. They were not much in favor of that. The king said they were likely making that choice which would be all the worse for them — "or which one of you was it that thought it most advisable to burn me in my hall?" Kjartan spoke up: "You no doubt think that the one who said this will not have the courage to own to it, but here you can see him." "See you I can indeed," said the king, "and a man of no small counsels either. But there will be no chance of your standing over the crown of my head. You have given me cause enough to see to it that you not threaten to burn any more kings in their halls, just because we would teach you something better. But since I don't know whether your heart was in what you said, and since you have owned to it like a man, I shall not take your life. It may also very well be that you who have spoken more against the faith than the others will keep it the more. I can also easily imagine that it will involve all the crews together, for the day when you let yourself be baptized of your own free will, they too no doubt will accept the faith. It also seems likely to me that your kinsmen and friends will heed what you have to say to them when you return to Iceland. And it is near my guess, Kjartan, that you will have a better faith when you sail from Norway than when you came here. Go now in peace and pardon, wherever you want to after this meeting. I shall not force the Christian faith upon you at this time, for God says that he wants no man to come to Him save of his own free will."

There was good applause for the king's speech, but to be sure mostly by the Christians. The heathens left it up to Kjartan to answer as he liked. Then Kjartan said: "We want to thank you, lord, for offering us safe conduct, and certainly you can best tempt us into accepting the new faith by giving up serious charges against us and speaking to us in this friendly manner, when on this day it lay in your hands to decide our fate as you pleased. But to this extent only do I intend to accept the faith in Norway: I'll put but little stock in Thór next winter when I get back to Iceland." Then the king smiled and said:

"One can see from the looks of Kjartan that he thinks he has better reason to put trust in his own strength and weapons than in Ódin and Thór." Then the Thing broke up.

After some time had passed, many people began prodding the king to force Kjartan and his men into accepting the faith, for they thought it unwise to have so many heathen men around. The king answered back sharply and said he was sure there were many Christians who were not nearly so praiseworthy in their conduct as Kjartan and his crew — "and for such men I can well afford to wait."

The king had many worthwhile things done that winter. He had a church built and had the town greatly enlarged. The church was finished by Yuletide. Kjartan told his men that they might go near enough to the church so as to be able to watch the ceremonies of this faith which the Christian men had. Many chimed in that it would be great sport. Kjartan went now with his group of men, and Bolli came too. Hallfred was also along, as well as many men from among the other Icelanders.

The king preached the faith before the people, both at length and eloquently, and the Christian men gave good applause for his sermon. When Kjartan and his companions had gone back to their quarters, much talk started up as to how they had liked the king on this day which Christian men call second only to their most holy festival[6] — "for the king said, so that we could hear, that that chieftain was born on this night in whom we are to believe if we do as the king bids us." Kjartan said: "So much did I like the king the first time I saw him, that I knew at once he was a most outstanding man; and later, whenever I saw him at gatherings of men, this has always held good. And yet I liked him much the best today, and I surmise that our whole welfare lies in our believing Him to be the true God whom the king proclaims. And now the king certainly cannot be more eager for me to accept the faith than I am to have myself baptized. There is only one thing that keeps me from going to see the king at once, and that is the lateness of the day, for the king will be at his table now, and it will certainly take a long day if all we comrades are to be baptized." Bolli fell in with this and said Kjartan alone was to decide.

The king had heard what Kjartan and his companions had talked about even before his tables were cleared away, for he had informers in all the quarters of the heathen men. The king was very happy at this news and said: "Kjartan has proved the adage that 'holy days are luckiest.'" And the very next morning early, when the king was going to church, Kjartan met him in the street with a great crowd of men. Kjartan greeted the king in all courtesy and said he had an urgent matter to take up with him. The king returned his greeting kindly and said he knew exactly what errand he was on — "and the matter can be easily taken care of for you." Kjartan begged the king not to delay then in getting to some water, saying there would be need for a great deal of it though. The king smiled and said: "Indeed, Kjartan, we would not come to disagreement over this, even if you drove a somewhat harder bargain."

Thereupon Kjartan and Bolli were baptized and all their crew, as well as many others. This took place before mass on the second day of Yule. After that the king asked Kjartan to his Yule feast, and also Bolli, his kinsman. Most people say that Kjartan was made Óláf's retainer the very day he laid aside his white baptismal gown,[7] he and Bolli together. Hallfred was not baptized that day, for he made the condition that the king himself should hold him under the baptismal water,[8] and the king arranged this for the next day. Kjartan and Bolli stayed with King Óláf all the rest of the winter. The king esteemed Kjartan above all men for his fine lineage and manly accomplishments. It was commonly said that Kjartan was so well liked that he had not a single ill-wisher at the court. It was also generally said that no man such as Kjartan had ever before come from Iceland. Bolli was also a most valiant man and highly esteemed by good men. Now the winter drew to a close, and when spring came, all who intended to go away got ready for their journeys.

41

Hostages, Scourgings, and Embargoes

KÁLF Ásgeirsson went to have a talk with Kjartan and asked him what he planned to do during the summer. Kjartan answered: "I rather thought we two might sail our ship to England, for Christian traders can find a good market there now. But I want to ask the king before I decide this definitely, for he wasn't too much in favor of my journey when we last talked about it in the spring."

Then Kálf walked away and Kjartan went to talk to the king and gave him a courteous greeting. The king received him kindly and asked what he and his comrades had been talking about. Kjartan said they had decided what they most wanted to do, but he had come nevertheless to ask leave for his journey. The king answered: "I will give you a choice in this, Kjartan — you may go out to Iceland this summer and convert the people to Christianity, by force or by persuasion. But if you feel this mission would be too hard for you to carry out, then in no case will I let you out of my hands, for in my estimation you are more suited to stay in the service of nobles here than to become a dealer in wares."

Kjartan chose rather to stay with the king than to go out to Iceland and preach the faith there, saying he had no desire to use force against his own kinsmen. "And as far as my father and other chieftains who are closely related to me are concerned, I daresay it will not be any more difficult to bring them round to your bidding when I am under your power in honorable service." The king replied: "You have made both a wise and manly choice." The king gave Kjartan a complete outfit of clothes newly cut from scarlet. They fitted him well, for people say that they were equally large men, when measured one against the other, King Óláf and Kjartan.

King Óláf sent his court priest by the name of Thangbrand to Iceland. He sailed his ship into the Álptafjord and stayed with Sídu-Hall[1] at Thvátta over the winter and preached the new faith to the people, with both persuasive words and severe scourgings. Thangbrand slew two men who were the most outspoken against the faith. Hall accepted the faith in the spring and was baptized on the Saturday before Easter together with all his household. And then Gizur the White had himself baptized and also Hjalti Skeggjason and many other chieftains. Still those numbered many more who held out against it, and it was anything but peaceful between the heathens and the Christians. The chieftains took counsel and decided that they would kill Thangbrand and all those who wanted to stand by him. In view of this hostility, Thangbrand took flight to Norway and went straightway to see King Óláf and told him to what pass his mission had come, and said that to his mind Christianity would never take root in Iceland. The king became very angry at this and said many Icelanders would get a taste of their own medicine unless they came to their senses of their own accord.

That same summer, Hjalti Skeggjason was outlawed at the Thing for blasphemy against the gods. Rúnólf Úlfsson, who lived at Dal by Eyjafjoll and was a great chieftain, was prosecutor of the case against him. The same summer Gizur went abroad and Hjalti with him. They made Norway and went straightway to see King Óláf. The king gave them good welcome, saying they had chosen the best way out and asked them to stay with him; and they accepted.

Sverting, the son of Rúnólf of Dal, had been in Norway during that winter and was bound for Iceland that summer. His ship was lying afloat by the pier, all set to sail, just waiting for a fair wind. The king put an embargo on his departure and said no ship would go to Iceland that summer. Sverting went to see the king and pleaded his case, asking leave for himself and saying that it made a great deal of difference to him that they not have to carry the lading off the ship again. The king was exceedingly wroth and replied: "It is just good enough for you, you son of an idolator, to have to stay where you like it least." So Sverting went nowhere. Nothing else to speak of happened that winter.

The following summer, the king sent Gizur the White and Hjalti Skeggjason to Iceland to preach the faith anew, but he kept four men behind as hostages — Kjartan Óláfsson; Halldór, son of Gudmund the Mighty; Kolbein, son of Thórd Freysgodi; and Sverting, son of Rúnólf of Dal. Then Bolli made up his mind to go with Gizur and Hjalti. So he went to find his kinsman Kjartan and said: "I am now ready to depart. I would like to wait for you over next winter, if, in the following summer, there would be any more chance of your getting away from here than there is now. But as far as we can see, the king isn't going to let you go on any account, and I take it for granted that you recall very little those pleasures which are to be had in Iceland when you are sitting talking to Ingibjorg, the king's sister."

She was then staying at King Óláf's court and was the fairest in the land. Kjartan answered: "Don't be saying such things, but bear my greetings to kinsmen and friends alike."

42

Laugar Again

AFTER that Kjartan and Bolli parted. Gizur and Hjalti sailed from Norway and had a good voyage. They arrived in the Vestmannaeyjar in time for the Thing and went to the mainland. There they met and talked with their kinsmen, and then went on to the Althing and preached the faith before the people, both at length and eloquently. Then all the people in Iceland accepted the faith.

Bolli rode from the Thing to Hjardarholt with his kinsman Óláf. Óláf received him with kindly affection. After he had been home a short while, Bolli rode to Laugar for some pastime, and he got good welcome there. Gudrún asked him all about his journey and then about Kjartan. Bolli replied obligingly to everything Gudrún asked about, and said that nothing to speak of had happened to him on his journey — "but as for Kjartan, certainly only the most praiseworthy things can be said, for he is at King Óláf's court and esteemed there above all others. And I wouldn't be at all surprised if we saw very little of him here in Iceland for the next few winters." Gudrún asked then if there were some reason for this, other than the friendship between Kjartan and the king. Bolli told her what sort of talk there had been about the friendship between Kjartan and Ingibjorg, the king's sister, and said that it was his guess that the king would rather give Ingibjorg to him in marriage than to let Kjartan go, if it came right down to it. Gudrún said that was all good news — "for Kjartan will only be worthily matched if he gets a fine woman." With this she abruptly let their talk drop and went away and was scarlet in the face. Others doubted whether this news really seemed so good to her as she let on.

Bolli stayed at home at Hjardarholt during the summer and had gained in honor from his journey. All his kinsmen and friends were greatly impressed with his gallantry. Bolli had also brought many wares with him out to Iceland. He went often to Laugar and talked with Gudrún. One time Bolli asked Gudrún what her answer would be if he made her a proposal. Gudrún was quick to answer: "There's no use talking about such a thing, Bolli. I will marry no man as long as I know Kjartan is alive." Bolli answered: "The way I see it, you will be sitting some years husbandless if you mean to wait for Kjartan. Besides he would have had a chance to entrust this matter to me, had it meant very much to him." They exchanged some words over this, but each would only see it his way. So Bolli rode home.

43

Ill-paid Friendship

SOME time later Bolli talked to his kinsman Óláf and said: "Things have come around to this, kinsman; I have made up my mind to settle down and get married. I consider myself a grown man now. I would like you to put in a good word for me and back up this suit, for there are a great many hereabouts who will honor what you say." Óláf answered: "I would say that most women would be getting more than a worthy offer where you are concerned. But you no doubt have not brought this matter up before you had it settled in your own mind where it was to land." Bolli answered: "I will not go outside the district to find a woman to ask, when there are such good matches so near at hand. It is Gudrún Ósvífsdóttir that I want to ask, for she is indeed the woman most coveted nowadays." Óláf answered: "This is one thing I want to have no part in. It is certainly no less known to you, Bolli, than to me, what talk there has been concerning the love between Kjartan and Gudrún. But if this makes such a great difference to you, then I will not stand in your way, assuming of course that you and Ósvíf can reach an agreement. Or have you perhaps talked this matter over already with Gudrún?" Bolli said he had hinted at it once, but she had shown little or no interest — "yet I daresay it will be Ósvíf who will have the most say in this." Óláf said Bolli might go about it as he saw fit.

Not long after that Bolli rode off from home, and with him were
Óláf's sons, Halldór and Steinthór. Altogether there were twelve in
the party. They rode to Laugar. Ósvíf and his sons bade them welcome. Bolli asked Ósvíf if he could have a talk with him and broached
the question of the proposal, asking for the hand of his daughter
Gudrún. Ósvíf gave this answer: "As you know, Bolli, Gudrún is a
widow and has the right to give her own answer, but I will see what
I can do." So Ósvíf went to have a talk with Gudrún and told her
that Bolli Thorleiksson had come there—"and he is asking for your
hand. Now it is up to you to answer his proposal, but I will be quick
in making my wish in this matter clear. Bolli is not to be turned
down if I am to have anything to say about it." Gudrún replied: "You
are very hasty in making up your mind about this. Besides, Bolli
once took this up with me, and I chose to refuse, and I am still of
the same mind." Then Ósvíf said: "Many people will say you speak
more out of prideful stubbornness than careful forethought if you say
'no' to such a man as Bolli. But as long as I am still alive, I shall see
to guiding you children of mine in those things where I am the
better judge." Seeing that Ósvíf was so set on the match, Gudrún
did not refuse outright, but nonetheless showed her unwillingness
on every hand. Ósvíf's sons urged it very much, for they thought the
match with Bolli would be much to their advantage. Be all that as
it may, the long and short of it was that the terms and the pledges
were settled and the date of the wedding feast fixed for the time of
the Winter Nights.[1] Then Bolli rode back to Hjardarholt and told
Óláf what had been arranged. Óláf had no comment. Bolli stayed
at home until it was time to go to the wedding. He invited his kinsman Óláf, and, though Óláf was in no humor to go, he went nonetheless at Bolli's pleading. It was a fine wedding feast at Laugar.
Afterwards Bolli stayed on there through the winter. There was not
much love lost in Bolli's and Gudrún's married life, at least not on
Gudrún's part.

When summer came, ships began passing between the countries.
Then the news got to Norway from Iceland that it was all Christian
now. King Óláf was greatly pleased about this and gave all those
men whom he had held as hostages permission to leave for Iceland
or wherever they chose. Kjartan answered, for he took the lead for

all those who had been held in hostage: "Do accept our thanks for this. It is our choice to visit Iceland this summer." Then King Óláf said: "I will not take back my word, Kjartan, but still what I said was meant more for the others than for you, for our feeling has been that you were staying here more as a friend than as a hostage. I wish your heart were not so set on going out to Iceland, even if you do have highly honored kinsmen there; for it will be yours for the asking to have a station in life here such as is not to be had in Iceland."[2]

Then Kjartan answered: "May the Lord reward you for the honor you have paid me since I came under your power. But I trust that you will grant leave to me no less than to those others whom you have been holding for some time." The king said it should be so, but added that it would be hard for him to find again among untitled men anyone to equal Kjartan.

That winter Kálf Ásgeirsson had been in Norway, having returned the previous fall from England with his and Kjartan's ship and wares. As soon as Kjartan had permission for the journey to Iceland, he and Kálf made ready to sail. When the ship was all ready, Kjartan went to see Ingibjorg, the king's sister. She gave him good welcome and made room for him to sit down beside her, and they fell to talking. When Kjartan told Ingibjorg all was in readiness for his journey to Iceland, she answered: "I'm rather inclined to think, Kjartan, that you have done this more out of willfulness than because anyone has urged you to leave Norway and go to Iceland." Few words passed between them after that.

Presently, Ingibjorg reached for a small treasure chest which stood near her and brought out a white headdress worked in gold and handed it to Kjartan: "It no doubt will be good enough for Gudrún Ósvífsdóttir to wrap around her head," she said, "and you can give it to her as a wedding gift.[3] I want the women in Iceland to see that she with whom you were wont to talk in Norway is not of lowly stock." There was a velvet case as a covering for the headdress, and it was altogether an ornament of rarest value. "I shall not go to see you off," said Ingibjorg. "Now fare well and luck be with you." After that Kjartan stood up and gave Ingibjorg a kiss. And if truth be told, people thought it hard for them to part.

Kjartan then left and went to tell the king that he was ready to

depart. King Óláf saw Kjartan off to the ship, and a large company
went down with him. And when they came to where the ship lay
afloat, with a single gangplank to shore, the king spoke up and said:
"Here is a sword, Kjartan, which I want you to accept as a parting
gift from me. Let it ever be at your side, for I venture to say that you
will never feel a weapon's fatal sting so long as you bear this sword." It
was a splendid weapon and richly ornamented. Kjartan thanked the
king with kind words for all the honor and esteem which had been
shown him while he was in Norway. Thereupon the king said: "This
will I beg of you, Kjartan, that you keep your faith well." Then the
king and Kjartan took leave of one another with warmest affection,
and Kjartan went aboard ship. The king stood and watched him go
and said: "Much is augured for Kjartan and his kin, and it will not
be easy to ward off their destiny."

44

Right Assumptions

AND so Kjartan and Kálf put out to sea. They had a good voyage and
were at sea but a short time and made the Hvítá in the Borgarfjord.
News of Kjartan's coming spread far and wide. His father Óláf and
other kinsmen heard it, and they were very happy about it. Óláf
rode east out of the Dales and on south to Borgarfjord. There was a
joyful meeting between father and son. Óláf asked Kjartan home
with him with as many men as he chose to bring. Kjartan was
pleased to accept and said this was the one place in Iceland where
he had counted on staying. Óláf now rode home to Hjardarholt, while
Kjartan stayed with the ship over the summer. It was then that he
learned of Gudrún's marriage, and contrary to what many had feared,
it did not seem to bother him.

Gudmund Solmundarson, Kjartan's brother-in-law, and his sister
Thúrid came out to the ship. Kjartan gave them good welcome.
Ásgeir Hothead also came to meet his son Kálf. His daughter Hrefna
was along in his party, and she was a most beautiful woman. Kjartan
told his sister Thuríd that she could take any of the wares she wanted,

and Kálf said the same to Hrefna. Kálf then opened up a large chest and told them to go over and have a look at it. During the day a sharp wind came up, and Kjartan and Kálf ran out to moor their ship. When they had finished, they went back to the booths. Kálf went back inside first. Thuríd and Hrefna had by then emptied much out of the chest. Just then Hrefna pulled out the headdress and was unfolding it. They were commenting on what a rare and costly thing it was, and Hrefna said she wanted to try it on. Thuríd thought that was a good idea, and so Hrefna put it on. Kálf saw this and said they were meddling with something they ought not to and told Hrefna to take it off at once — "for this is the one thing that Kjartan and I do not own in common."

Just as they were talking about this, Kjartan came into the booth. He had heard what they were saying and quickly interjected that no harm was done. Hrefna was still sitting with the headdress on. Kjartan looked at her long and closely and said: "The headdress is very becoming to you, Hrefna, and I don't think it would be a bad idea if I owned both together, the bonnet and the bonnie lass." Then Hrefna answered: "It's generally assumed that you will not want to look for a wife very soon, but will get the woman you ask." Kjartan replied that it would not matter much whom he got, but one thing was sure, he would not pay court and be kept waiting long. "I see that this attire suits you very well, and it is no doubt fitting that you become my wife." Then Hrefna took off the headdress and handed it to Kjartan, and he put it away for safekeeping.

Gudmund and Thuríd invited Kjartan to visit them up north during the winter. Kjartan promised to come. Kálf Ásgeirsson decided to go with his father. So he and Kjartan dissolved their partnership, and that went off smoothly and good-naturedly. Kjartan rode then from the ship and set off westward for the Dales. There were twelve in his party. When he came home to Hjardarholt, all were happy to see him. In the fall he had his goods from the ship moved north. All twelve of the men who rode west with Kjartan stayed at Hjardarholt through the winter.

Óláf and Ósvíf had kept up their custom of inviting one another back and forth. Every fall one of them was to visit the other. This fall the feast was to be at Laugar, and Óláf and the Hjardholters were

to come. Gudrún now said to Bolli that it looked as though he had
not told her the whole truth in connection with Kjartan's return to
Iceland. Bolli said he had told her to the best of his knowledge.
Gudrún had little to say on the subject, but it was plain to see that
she took it in ill-humor, and most people suspected that she still
cared a great deal for Kjartan, even if she covered it up.

The time now came when the fall feast at Laugar was to take
place. Óláf got himself ready to go and asked Kjartan to come along.
Kjartan said he would stay at home to take care of the farm. Óláf
begged him not to bear hard feelings against his kinsman. "Remember this, Kjartan, that there has never been anyone whom you have
loved so much as your foster brother Bolli. I would like you to go
along. You two will soon be reconciled if you but get together again."
Kjartan did as his father wished. He took out his scarlet clothes which
King Óláf had given him at parting,[1] and dressed himself in all his
finery. He girded himself with the sword Konungsnaut,[2] the king's
gift, and had a gilt helmet on his head and a red shield at his side
with the holy cross traced in gold, and in his hand he carried a spear
with a gold-inlaid socket. All his men were in brightly colored array.[3]
They made up a party of about thirty altogether. So now they rode
forth out of Hjardarholt and on to Laugar. There they found a large
gathering awaiting them.

45

Resentment and Rebound

BOLLI, as well as Ósvíf's sons, went out to meet Óláf and his party
and gave them a fine welcome. Bolli went over to Kjartan and gave
him a kiss, and Kjartan acknowledged his greeting. After that they
were seen into the house. Bolli was in the best of spirits, friendly and
cheerful toward them, which Óláf took exceedingly well, but Kjartan rather coolly.

The feast got off to a good start. Bolli had some studhorses which
were deemed the very finest. The stallion was a large and splendid
animal and had never been beaten in a horse fight. He was all white

except for his red ears and forelock. Three mares of the same color-
ing as the stallion made up the stud. These horses Bolli wanted to
give to Kjartan, but Kjartan said he was no horse groomer and
would not accept. Óláf begged him to take the horses — "for they are
a most honorable gift." Kjartan replied with a flat "no." Thereupon
they parted with hard feelings and the Hjardholters rode home. Then
everything remained quiet.

Kjartan was rather moody during the winter, and nobody got much
talk out of him. To Óláf this seemed a great pity. That winter after
Yule, Kjartan prepared to set out from home. There were twelve of
them altogether who planned to go up to the north district. They
rode along on their way until they came to Vídidal in the north, and
to Ásbjarnarnes, where Kjartan was given a cheerful and hearty welcome. The farm had very fine buildings and living quarters. Hall,
Gudmund's son, was then in his twenties and took very much after
his Laxárdal kin. It was generally said that there had never been a
more valiant man in the North Quarter.[1] Hall gave his kinsman
Kjartan a very friendly welcome. Presently games got underway at
Ásbjarnarnes, and people assembled from far and wide around the
countryside. They came from the west out of Midfjord and from
Vatnsnes and Vatnsdal and all the way from Langadal. A great crowd
gathered there. All people could talk about was what a paragon
among men Kjartan was. Then the games began, and Hall acted as
leader. He asked Kjartan to join in — "We would like you to show
us your chivalrous talents, kinsman." Kjartan replied: "I have done
but little practicing at games of late, for there were usually other
things to do at King Óláf's court. But for just this once I'll not refuse
you."

Kjartan now got himself ready for the competitions. The strongest
men there were matched against him. The games continued throughout the day. Not a man there had the strength or agile skill to equal
Kjartan's. And when night fell, the games were brought to a close,
and Hall Gudmundarson stood up to speak: "It is my father's wish
to invite all those who have come here from farthest away to stay
overnight and take up the merrymaking here again tomorrow." This
invitation brought good applause and it was thought a generous one.

Kálf Ásgeirsson had come there, and he and Kjartan liked one another very much. Kálf's sister Hrefna was also there. She was very fond of decking herself out in fine clothes. More than a hundred people stayed at the farm overnight. The next day games were taken up again. Kjartan was sitting at the side and looking on. Then his sister Thuríd went over to talk to him and had this to say: "I've been told, kinsman, that you have been rather glum all winter; and talk has it that you probably still care for Gudrún, and this they adduce from the fact that there's no longer any happy friendship between you and your kinsman Bolli, in spite of the great fondness there had always been between you. Please act nice and don't take it so to heart. You shouldn't begrudge your kinsman his good match. We feel the most advisable thing for you to do is to take a wife, as you said you would last summer, even if Hrefna isn't an equal match for you in every respect; for you can never expect to find that here in this country. Her father Ásgeir is an honorable man and of high birth, and doesn't lack for wealth either to make this match an attractive one. And another daughter of his is married to a powerful man. You have also told me yourself that Kálf Ásgeirsson is the most stalwart of fellows. All in all they live in highest estate. I wish you'd have a talk with Hrefna, and I wouldn't wonder if you'd find brains to match her beauty."

Kjartan fell in with this and said she had presented her point well. After that he and Hrefna got together for a talk; they visited throughout the day. In the evening Thuríd asked Kjartan what he had thought of Hrefna after his talk with her. He said he was well pleased and that she seemed to be an unusual woman in every respect, as far as he could tell. The next morning men were sent to Ásgeir, and he was asked to come to Ásbjarnarnes. Thereupon they took this matter up and Kjartan asked for the hand of Hrefna, Ásgeir's daughter. He was most favorable to this proposal, for he was a sensible man and could see what an honorable offer was being made them. Kálf urged it very much, saying — "There is nothing I wouldn't do to bring this about."

Hrefna, for her part, did not refuse either and told her father to decide. The matter was now settled and made binding with witnesses. Kjartan would have it no other way but that the wedding be at Hjardarholt, and Ásgeir and Kálf did not object. Then the wedding was set to take place at Hjardarholt after five weeks of summer had passed. After that Kjartan rode home with splendid gifts. Óláf was well pleased upon hearing this news, for Kjartan was in much brighter spirits now than when he had left for the north.

Kjartan kept dry fast[2] during Lent; and thus did what no man had ever done before him in this country; for people say he was the first man here in this land to have so fasted. People thought it so strange that Kjartan lived such a long time meatless that they came long distances just to look at him. Likewise Kjartan's other manners and ways outshone those of other men. Then Easter came and went. After that Kjartan and Óláf made preparations for the big feast.

Ásgeir and Kálf, and Gudmund and Hall came down from the north at the appointed time, and there were sixty altogether in their party. Kjartan and Óláf also had a large gathering there to greet them. The feast was a splendid one, and lasted a week. Kjartan gave Hrefna the headdress as a bridal gift, and this present was the subject of much talk, for no one there, no matter how wise or wealthy, had ever seen or owned such a priceless treasure. According to those versed in such things, eight ounces of gold were woven into the headdress. Kjartan too was in such high spirits at the feast that he put everyone in a merry mood with the tales of his journeys. They all made much over the marvelous adventures of which he had to tell, for he had been a long time in the service of one of the most famous chieftains, King Óláf Tryggvason.

When the feast was over, Kjartan selected handsome gifts for Gudmund and Hall and other prominent guests. Father and son gained much renown from this feast, and Kjartan and Hrefna came to love one another dearly.

46

A King's Sword and a Queenly Headdress

ÓLÁF and Ósvíf held to their friendship as before, even though there was some friction between the young people. That summer Óláf was to hold a feast at his farm half a month before winter set in. Ósvíf likewise had a feast planned for the time of the Winter Nights. Each asked the other to come with as many guests as would do him the most honor. So it was Ósvíf's turn to come to Óláf first, and he came to Hjardarholt at the appointed time. In his company were Bolli and Gudrún and his sons. The following morning as the women were walking down the length of the hall past the sleeping quarters, one of them raised the question about how the women were to be seated. It happened that Gudrún was walking along just opposite the bed-closet that was Kjartan's and where even then he was getting dressed and putting on his red-scarlet kirtle. Before anyone else had a chance to answer, Kjartan called out to the woman who had been talking about the seating arrangement: "Hrefna is to sit in the high-seat and altogether be the most honored as long as I am alive." (But before, it had always been Gudrún who had occupied the high-seat, both at Hjardarholt and elsewhere.) Gudrún overheard this and looked at Kjartan and turned red, but said nothing.

The next day Gudrún suggested to Hrefna that she put on the headdress and show the people this fabulous adornment, the likes of which had never before been seen in Iceland. Kjartan was standing a little way off, yet within earshot, and overheard what Gudrún said. He spoke up before Hrefna had a chance to answer: "She is not to put on the headdress at this feast, for I deem it more important that Hrefna own this most costly treasure than that the guests now have the pleasure of laying eyes on it."

The feast that fall at Óláf's was to last the week. Again on the next day Gudrún asked Hrefna on the sly to show her the headdress. Hrefna promised to do so. Later in the day they went out to the storehouse where the valuables were kept. Hrefna opened up a chest and brought out the velvet case and pulled out the headdress and showed it to Gudrún. Gudrún spread it out and looked at it for some time, but had not a word to say, neither praise nor blame. Then Hrefna stored it away again, and they went back to their places. Thereafter all was mirth and merrymaking.

On the day the guests were to ride away, Kjartan was much occupied with arranging for horses for the people who had come a long way, and taking care of each one's needs for his journey. Kjartan had not been carrying his sword Konungsnaut around with him while

going about these duties, although he was rarely in the habit of letting it very far out of his sight. Afterwards, he went back to his bedcloset where he had left the sword, and it was gone. Straightway he
went to tell his father of this loss. Óláf said: "We shall go about this
as quietly as possible, and I will get men to go along and be on the
lookout in each of the groups that rides away." And that's what he
did.

Án the White was to ride along in Ósvíf's party and keep an eye
out for anyone who might turn off to the side or lag behind. They
rode in along the Ljárskógar and by those farms called Skógar and
stopped there and got off their horses. Thórólf, Ósvíf's son, struck off
in a direction away from the farmstead and some other men with him.
They disappeared into some brushwood while the others tarried at
Skógar. Án kept them company as far as the Laxá where it flows out
from Saelingsdal, and then said he would turn back. Thórólf said it
would not have done any harm, had he not gone any place at all.
The night before a light snow had fallen so that it was easy to see
tracks. Án rode back to the woods and traced Thórólf's footprints to a
swamp or boggy place. He groped around down in the mire and felt
the hilt of a sword. Án wanted to have witnesses to this incident and
rode to fetch Thórarin in Saelingsdalstunga, and he went back with
Án to take up the sword. After that Án brought the sword to Kjartan.
Kjartan wrapped it up in a cloth and laid it away in a chest. The
place where Thórólf and the others had hidden Konungsnaut has
been called Sverdskelda (Sword Swamp) ever since. Now it was
quiet and the matter was dropped, but the scabbard was never found
afterwards, and Kjartan never took the same pride in the sword as
he had before.

This whole affair rankled deep down in Kjartan and he did not
want to let the matter stand. But Óláf told him: "Don't let this rankle
with you. They have played a mean trick, but there's no harm done
you. Let's not make a laughingstock out of ourselves by quarreling
over such a thing, especially when it is all between kinsmen and
friends." After Óláf put it that way, Kjartan let matters be.

Presently Óláf got ready to attend the feast at Laugar at the time
of the Winter Nights. He spoke to Kjartan about it and told him he
ought to go. Kjartan held back but nonetheless promised to go after

his father's pleading. Hrefna was to go too, but wanted to leave her headdress at home. However, Thorgerd, the mistress of the house, put it to her this way: "When are you ever going to make use of such finery, if it is to be left behind at home in a chest when you go to feasts?" Hrefna answered: "There are those who say that I could find many places to go where I would have fewer ill-wishers than at Laugar." Thorgerd said: "I don't put much stock in people who peddle such gossip between the farms here." So because Thorgerd was so set on it, Hrefna took the headdress along. Kjartan did not oppose it when he saw how much his mother wished it.

They started out on their way and arrived at Laugar by nightfall where they were given a fine welcome. Thorgerd and Hrefna handed over their clothing to be taken care of. But in the morning when the women were to put on their finery, Hrefna looked for her headdress and it was gone from where she had put it away. They searched high and low for it but it could not be found. Gudrún said most likely it had been left behind at home, or she might have packed it carelessly and dropped it on the way. Hrefna now told Kjartan that the headdress had disappeared. He replied by saying it was no easy job to be constantly on guard with these people, and bade her keep the matter quiet. Later he told his father what was afoot. Óláf replied: "I would still like you to let matters ride as we did before and go on as though nothing had happened. I will look into this quietly for I would do anything so that it didn't come to an open breach between you and Bolli. 'It's easier to bind what is whole, kinsman,'" he said. Kjartan replied: "It is obvious, father, that you mean only the best for everyone out of this, but still I don't know whether I like leaning over backwards for these Laugar folk all the time."

Then when everyone was to ride away from the feast, Kjartan spoke up and said: "I'm calling you to account, kinsman Bolli; henceforth you'll have to show yourself more willing to treat us decently than you have up until now. I am not going to keep this hushed up either, for it is now common knowledge that things have been disappearing hereabouts which we believe have found their way into your keep. In the fall when we held a feast at Hjardarholt, a sword of mine was stolen. It came back, but not the scabbard. And here again a costly thing has disappeared which is deemed of rarest value. I now want both of them back."

Then Bolli answered: "We are not guilty of what you accuse us, Kjartan. We would have expected anything else of you but that you would charge us with stealing." Kjartan said: "We have good cause to believe that those people who have been involved in this incident are near enough so that you can make things good if you but want to. You are provoking us more than there is any call for. We have long put up with your hostility. But now I want it understood that that will no longer do."

Then Gudrún gave him answer and said: "Now you are raking up a fire, Kjartan, which were better not to smoke. But even if it be as you say, that there are some people here who have taken it upon themselves to see to the disappearance of the headdress, then I would judge they have only come by what was theirs. Now you may think what you like about what has become of the headdress, but it won't seem ill to me if it has been so taken care of that Hrefna will have little good of it from now on."

After this they parted, with hard feelings on both sides, and the Hjardholters rode home. The partying back and forth came to an end; yet things stayed quiet, so to speak. No trace of the headdress was ever found. Many people thought the truth of the matter was that Thórólf had burned it on the advice of his sister Gudrún. At the beginning of that winter Ásgeir Hothead died, and his sons took over his estate and goods.

47

Retaliation

THAT winter after Yule, Kjartan gathered some men together, sixty in all. He did not tell his father what these preparations of his were all about, and Óláf did not ask much about it either. Kjartan took along tents and provisions and continued on his way until he came to Laugar. He ordered his men to dismount and told some of them to look after the horses and others to put up the tents. It was cus-

tomary at that time to have an outdoor privy, some distance from the
house, and so it was at Laugar. Kjartan stationed guards at all the
doors of the farmhouse and barred the exit of all persons, so that they
had to relieve themselves indoors for three days and nights. After
that Kjartan rode home to Hjardarholt and his followers went their
own ways.

Óláf voiced his disapproval of this venture. Thorgerd said there
was no call for censuring, declaring that the Laugar folk had merited
just that and even greater indignity. And Hrefna said "Did you talk
with anyone at Laugar, Kjartan?" He and Bolli had exchanged a few
words, he said, "but it didn't amount to much." Then Hrefna smiled
and said: "I've been told as a matter of fact that you and Gudrún
talked with one another, and I have even heard what she had on.
She had herself decked out in the headdress and it suited her exceedingly well." Kjartan turned very red at this—it was plain for everyone to see that he was angry that she made such sport of this. "Nothing of what you say, Hrefna, has come before my eyes," he replied.
"Besides Gudrún would not need to deck herself out in the headdress
in order to look lovelier than all other women." With that Hrefna
broke off talking.

The Laugar folk were ill-content and felt this to be more of a
disgrace and a far worse one than if Kjartan had outright killed a
man or two of them. Ósvíf's sons were the most wrought up over this,
but Bolli more or less calmed them down. Gudrún said the least
about it; but even so, from what little she did say, people were not so
sure that it went any less deeply with her than with the others. Now
it came to open hostility between the Laugar folk and the Hjardholters. When the winter was nearly over, Hrefna gave birth to a
child. It was a boy and he was called Ásgeir.

Thórarin, the farmer at Tunga, let it be known that he wanted to
sell the Tunga lands. This was on two accounts—his livestock was
dwindling, and he thought there was too much friction developing
between the people in the district, and he was a friend to both
sides. Bolli felt he needed to buy himself a piece of land of his own,
for the Laugar folk had little land, but much livestock. Bolli and
Gudrún rode to Tunga at Ósvíf's suggestion. It seemed just meant

for them to take up this land right adjacent to theirs, and Ósvíf told them not to let any trifle stand in the way. They talked the sale over with Thórarin and came to an agreement as to what it would cost and how it was to be paid, and a bargain was struck between them. But since there were not enough people present to make it binding before the law, the sale was not closed by witnesses. After that Bolli and Gudrún rode back home.

When Kjartan Óláfsson heard this news, he rode off at once in a party of twelve and arrived at Tunga early in the day. Thórarin gave him good welcome and invited him to stay overnight. Kjartan said he would be riding back home the same evening, but would stay for a while. Thórarin asked what errand he was on. Kjartan answered: "I've come here to talk about a certain land sale which you and Bolli have agreed on, for it's not to my liking that you sell this land to Bolli and Gudrún." Thórarin said anything else now would be awkward for him — "for the price which Bolli has promised to pay for the land is a very good one and it is to be paid up quickly." Kjartan replied: "It will not be to your loss if Bolli doesn't buy the land, for I will buy it at the same price. And there is no use in your making any objection to what I want done, for you'll soon see that I mean to have the most to say in this district, and if I do anything to please anybody, it will by no means be the Laugar folk." Thórarin replied: "With me the master's word is law; but it would be more to my liking if the sale that Bolli and I have agreed on stands as it is." Kjartan said: "I don't call that a sale of land when it isn't bound by witnesses. Now you can do one of two things — either give me your hand right here and now on the sale of this land on the same terms as you have agreed upon with others, or stay put on your land yourself." Thórarin chose to sell him the land. This time there were witnesses at the sale. Having bought the land, Kjartan rode back home.

This was rumored throughout the Breidafjord Dales. That very same evening the news got to Laugar, whereupon Gudrún said: "It seems to me, Bolli, as if Kjartan were also giving you two choices, and somewhat harder ones than he gave Thórarin. Either you will be made to leave this district with little honor, or else you will have to show yourself somewhat less easygoing than you have up until now, whenever you two meet again." Bolli said not a word and walked away. Things now remained quiet through the rest of Lent.

The third day of Easter week, Kjartan set off from home with but one other man. It was Án the Black who went with him. They came to Tunga that day. Kjartan wanted Thórarin to ride along with him west to Saurbaer to confirm some outstanding debts, for Kjartan had some money matters to tend to there. Thórarin, however, had ridden over to a neighboring farm, so Kjartan stopped over for a while and waited for him. That same day Thórhalla Chatterbox also happened by. She asked Kjartan where he was bound for. He said he would be going west to Saurbaer. "Which road are you going to take?" she asked. "I'll ride west by way of Saelingsdal, and east by way of Svínadal," answered Kjartan. She asked how long he would be. Kjartan replied: "I'll most likely ride east on Thursday." "Could you do an errand for me?" asked Thórhalla. "I have a kinsman west of Hvítadal in Saurbaer, and he has promised me half a mark's worth of homespun.[1] I would like you to pick it up and bring it along when you come from the west." Kjartan promised to do that. Then Thórarin came home and decided to go along with Kjartan and Án. They rode west over the moors of the Saelingsdalsheidi and came to Hól that evening to stay with the two brothers Thorkel and Knút and their sister Aud. Kjartan was given a fine welcome, for they were all very good friends.

That evening Thórhalla Chatterbox came home to Laugar. Ósvíf's sons asked whom she had chanced to meet during the day. She said she had happened upon Kjartan Óláfsson. They asked her where he was bound for. She related what she knew — "and never has he been more gallant than today; it's not at all to be wondered at that such people stick their noses up at everything else." And Thórhalla went on: "That seemed to me all the more clear, as Kjartan liked nothing better than to talk about his and Thórarin's land sale." Gudrún spoke up: "It certainly looks as though Kjartan could go right ahead and do anything he pleases, for no matter what insulting thing he does, nobody even dares to shake a stick at him." Both Bolli and Ósvíf's sons were within hearing of this exchange between Thórhalla and Gudrún. Óspak and the others had little to say, but what they did say was more a berating of Kjartan than anything else — as was usual with

them. Bolli acted as if he had not heard, for Bolli always had a way
of either keeping still or objecting whenever Kjartan was ill-spoken
of.

48

Gudrún's Goading

THE FOURTH day of Easter Kjartan was still at Hól. There was much
merrymaking and gaiety. That night Án slept restlessly and was
roused from his sleep. They asked him what he had been dreaming.
He answered: "Some horrible-looking woman came to me and pulled
me out onto the front rail of my bed. She had a large knife in one
hand and a trough in the other.[1] She drove the knife into my chest
and slashed my whole belly open and took out the bowels and
stuffed brushwood in instead. After that she went out," said Án.

Kjartan and the others had a good laugh at his dream and said he
ought to be called Án Brushwood Belly, and then they started tussling
with him, saying they wanted to feel whether or not there were
brambles in his belly. Then Aud said: "There's no call for poking so
much fun at this. My advice is that Kjartan should do one of two
things — either stay here longer, or if he insists on going, then he
should ride away with more in his company than he came with."
"Maybe you think Án Brushwood Belly is a man of wise words,"
says Kjartan, "when he sits around here all day talking to you, for
you seem to take everything he dreams as some portent. But I am
going to go ahead just as I planned, for all this dream."

Kjartan set out early on the fifth day of Easter week, and Thorkel
Hvelp and his brother Knút went too on Aud's insistence. There were
twelve altogether who rode out with Kjartan. Kjartan came by
Hvítadal and fetched the homespun for Thórhalla Chatterbox as he
had promised. Then he rode south by way of Svínadal.

But let us see what was going on at Laugar in Saelingsdal. Gudrún
was up and about early, as soon as the sun had risen. She went to
where her brothers were sleeping and shook Óspak. He woke up at
once, as did some of the others. And when Óspak saw that it was his

sister, he asked what she wanted, up and about so early. Gudrún said she wanted to know how they intended to spend the day. Óspak said they would not be stirring about much — "for there is little on hand to do right now." Gudrún retorted: "It would have suited you just right to be daughters of some farmer or other, the way you act, not turning a hand either to help or hinder. Such insult and shame as Kjartan has done to you, and you can nonetheless go on sleeping when he may be riding right past your door with but one man in his company. The likes of you have memories about as long as a swine's. As far as I can see there's no hope of your ever getting up enough courage to attack Kjartan on his home grounds, if you don't even dare to meet up with him now when he is traveling with but a man or two. But you just sit at home making empty promises and are too many for any good use."

Óspak said she was making too much of this, but that he was hard put for an argument. So he jumped up at once and dressed, as did each of the brothers one after the other. They then laid plans to waylay Kjartan, and Gudrún asked Bolli to go along with them. Bolli said it was not right for him to go, because of his kinship with Kjartan, and reminded her with what loving kindness Óláf had brought him up. Gudrún answered: "What you say is true, but it can't be your good fortune to please everybody all of the time. And our life together will be finished if you refuse this." When Gudrún put it that way, all the hateful things he had suffered at Kjartan's hands loomed large inside Bolli and he quickly took up his weapons. They came to nine altogether. Ósvíf's five sons were there — Óspak and Helgi, Vandrád and Torrád, and Thórólf. Bolli made the sixth, and Gudlaug, the son of Ósvíf's sister and a most promising man, was the seventh. Then there were Odd and Stein, Thórhalla Chatterbox' sons. They rode to Svínadal and took up their position by the gully which is called Hafragil. They tied up their horses and sat down to wait. Bolli was silent all the day and lay up on the brink of the gulch.

Now when Kjartan and his party had come on south past Mjósyndi where the valley begins to widen out, Kjartan said that Thorkel and the others might as well turn back. Thorkel said they would ride up to where the valley came to an end. But when they had got on south past the mountain dairies called Nordrsel, Kjartan again told the brothers that they need not ride any further — "Thórólf, that thief, isn't going to have the laugh on me for not daring to go on ahead with only a few men along." Thorkel Hvelp answered: "We will give in to you now and not ride along any further. But we will regret it very much if you should have need of men today and are not with you." Then Kjartan said: "Never will my kinsman Bolli be party to a plot against my life. And if Ósvíf's sons are lying in wait for me, there's no predicting which of us will live to tell the tale, even though the odds are against me." So the brothers and their party rode back west.

49

The Curse of Footbite

So THEY came riding south down the valley, the three of them together — Kjartan, Án the Black, and Thórarin. There was a man called Thorkel who lived at Hafratindar in Svínadal, a place now deserted. He had gone to see to his horses that day, and his shepherd boy with him. They saw both parties, the Laugar men lying in wait and Kjartan and his companions as they came riding down the valley, three together. The shepherd lad spoke up and said they ought to head off Kjartan and his party, that it was a stroke of luck if he and Thorkel could prevent such great trouble as otherwise was sure to happen. Thorkel said: "Hold your tongue! Are you fool enough to think you can save a man's life if he be doomed to die? And to tell you the truth, I wouldn't put myself out for either one of them. For all I care, they may as well deal as foully with one another as they please. A better plan, it seems to me, would be for us to get ourselves to a place where we will be out of danger but can watch the skirmish to best advantage and have some fun for ourselves out of their sport. For everyone brags that Kjartan puts up a better fight than most. I wouldn't doubt but what he will stand in need of his skill now, for no one knows better than you and I how great the odds are." And so it came to be as Thorkel wished.

Kjartan and his companions kept on riding toward Hafragil. Mean-

while Ósvíf's sons began to have their suspicions as to why Bolli
sought out such a place for himself where he could easily be seen by
anyone riding from the west. They took counsel together and it
seemed to them that Bolli very likely could be playing them false,
so they went up to him on the slope and began bantering and boxing
around with him and took him by the heels and dragged him down
the slope.

Meantime Kjartan and his men were fast approaching, as they were
riding hard. And just as they were coming south of the gulch, they
caught sight of the ambush and recognized the men. Kjartan at
once jumped down from his horse and turned upon Ósvíf's sons.
There was a big boulder standing nearby, and there Kjartan said they
would take their stand. But before the hand to hand fighting began,
Kjartan flung his spear, and it landed in Thórólf's shield just above
the handstrap and pinned the shield to him, as the spear had pierced
through the shield and gone into his arm above the elbow, ripping
apart the main muscle. With that Thórólf let loose of the shield and
had no use of his arm the rest of the day. Then Kjartan drew his
sword, but he had not Konungsnaut. Thórhalla's sons made a run
at Thórarin, as that was the task allotted to them. It was a tough
fight, for Thórarin had stamina and the other two were also hardy
fighters. One could scarcely venture a guess as to who would come
out ahead. Then Ósvíf's sons and Gudlaug set on Kjartan. They were
five to Kjartan's and Án's two.[1] Án put up a good fight and was always
going out in front to cover Kjartan. Bolli was standing off aloof with
Footbite in his hand. Kjartan smote hard, but his sword was not much
good; time and again he had to straighten the blade under his foot.
Presently both sides got wounded, Ósvíf's sons and Án. Kjartan had
no wound as yet. He fought so fast and furiously that Gudlaug and
Ósvíf's sons backed away and turned to where Án was. Then Án
fell, having kept right on fighting for some time, even though his
bowels were coming out. At that moment Kjartan struck off Gudlaug's leg above the knee, and that blow was enough to kill him.

Then the four sons of Ósvíf attacked Kjartan, but he put up such
a good fight that he gave not an inch of ground before them. Then
Kjartan called out: "Kinsman Bolli, why did you bother to leave
home, if you only mean to stand quietly by? It is now time for you

to lend a hand to one or the other of us and try out how good Footbite is." Bolli pretended he had not heard. As soon as Óspak saw
that they could never get Kjartan down, he started egging Bolli on
in every way he could, telling him that he surely would not want
to face the shame of having promised them backing in the fight and
then not have given it — "and remember Kjartan dealt sorely with us
when we hadn't done anything nearly as bad. If Kjartan gets away
now, Bolli, that means your undoing as well as ours in no time at
all." So now Bolli draws Footbite and turns on Kjartan.

Then Kjartan said to Bolli: "It is certainly a dastard's deed you
mean to do now, kinsman. But it seems to me far better to receive
death at your hand, kinsman, than to deal it to you." With that
Kjartan threw down his weapons and had no will to defend himself,
little wounded though he was, although to be sure he was battle
weary. Bolli made no reply to Kjartan's words, but dealt him the death
blow all the same. No sooner had he done it than he sat down with
Kjartan's shoulders in his lap, and there on Bolli's knees Kjartan
breathed his last.

Almost the moment he did it, Bolli regretted his deed and gave
witness to this killing by his hand. Bolli then sent Ósvíf's sons back
to the farm district, while he and Thórarin stayed behind with the
dead. And when Ósvíf's sons got to Laugar, they told what had happened. Gudrún voiced her approval of it. Thórólf's arm was then
bound up; it was slow to heal and was never completely well again.

Kjartan's body was brought back to Tunga. After that Bolli rode
home to Laugar. Gudrún went out to meet him and asked him how
late in the day it was. Bolli said it was almost noonday. Then Gudrún said: "The seeds of discontent have certainly borne great fruit —
I have spun twelve ells of yarn, and you have killed Kjartan."[2]
Bolli answered: "It's going to take a long enough time as it is for me
to forget that mishap, without your having to remind me of it."
Gudrún said: "Such a thing I would not count among mishaps. It
seemed to me that you enjoyed greater esteem that winter when
Kjartan was in Norway than afterwards when he returned to Iceland
and trod you underfoot. And last but not least, what means the most
to me is that Hrefna will not be laughing when she goes to bed
tonight." Then Bolli replied and was exceedingly wroth: "I have my

doubts that she will turn any more pale at these tidings than you, and I'm not so sure but what it would have been a lesser shock to you if we all were lying out on the battle ground and Kjartan had brought you the news." Gudrún, realizing then how angry Bolli was, said: "Don't be saying such things, for I am grateful for what you have done. I think you have shown me now that there's nothing you wouldn't do for me."

Thereafter Ósvíf's sons went into hiding in an underground hide-out which had been secretly built for them, whereas Thórhalla's sons were sent off to Helgafell to tell Snorri Godi this news and ask him to send them immediate aid as backing against Óláf and those who had to take up the prosecution for Kjartan's slaying.

At Saelingsdalstunga, the night following the day of the slaying, a strange thing happened. Án, whom all took to be dead, suddenly sat up. All those who were keeping vigil with the dead were frightened and thought it a strange wonder. Then Án spoke to them: "I beg of you in God's name not to be afraid of me, for I have been alive all along and have had all my wits about me up until the time when I fell into a deep swoon. Then I dreamt about the same woman as before, and now methought she took the brushwood out of my belly and put my bowels back instead, and I felt good with that exchange." After that Án's wounds were bound up and he got well and was called Án Brushwood Belly ever after.

When Óláf Hoskuldsson heard these tidings, he was sorely stricken over Kjartan's slaying but nonetheless bore up bravely. His sons wanted to go after Bolli at once and kill him. But Óláf said: "That is far from my will; it won't bring back my son, even if Bolli is slain. I loved Kjartan above and beyond anyone else, but I cannot bear to see any harm come to Bolli. However, I know a more fitting task that you can do. Go and overtake Thórhalla's sons who are on their way to Helgafell to gather forces against us. Whatever punishment you see fit to mete out to them will be to my liking."

Thereupon Óláf's sons swiftly got started on their way and boarded a ferry which Óláf owned. They were seven altogether. They rowed out along Hvammsfjord and pushed on with all their might and main. They had a light but fair wind. They rowed under sail until they came down along the isle of Skorey and stopped there for a while and asked around about any travelings of people in those parts. And a little later they caught sight of a ship rowing out from the west across the fjord. They soon recognized the men — they were Thórhalla's sons all right. Halldór Óláfsson and the others set out at once after them. They put up no resistance, for Óláf's sons leapt aboard their ship before they knew what was happening. Stein and his brother were seized, killed, and thrown overboard. Óláf's sons turned back, and their mission was thought most successful.

50

A Bid for Peace

ÓLÁF went out to meet Kjartan's body. He sent men south to Borg to tell Thorstein Egilsson what had happened and also that he wanted to have his backing for the prosecution of the case. He wanted to have everything in hand, he said, should any of the powerful men join up with Ósvíf's sons against him. He sent word to the same effect up north to Vídidal, to his son-in-law Gudmund, and to Ásgeir's sons, informing them too that he had charged everyone with Kjartan's killing who had been in on the ambush, all except Óspak Ósvífsson. He was already outlawed as it was, on account of a certain woman by the name of Aldís, who was the daughter of Hólmgongu-Ljót from Ingjaldssand. Their son was Úlf, who later was Lord Marshall under King Harald Sigurdarson. He had Jórunn Thorbergsdóttir as a wife. Their son was Jón, who was the father of Erlend Hímaldi (Laggard), who was the father of Eystein the Archbishop. Óláf had given notice that the charges for manslaughter would be made at the Thórsnes Thing. He had Kjartan's body moved on home and a tent put up over it, for at that time no church had as yet been built in the Dales.

As soon as Óláf learned that Thorstein had been quick to act and was coming on with a strong force and that the Víddalers had done likewise, Óláf summoned men from all over the Dales, and they came to a great number. Óláf then sent this whole force off to Laugar, saying: "It is my wish that you defend Bolli if need be —

and no less so than if you were standing by me — for if I don't miss my guess those from outside the district, whom we will have on our hands any time now, will feel that they have a score of their own to settle with Bolli."

Directly after all this was arranged, Thorstein and his men arrived and also the Víddalers, and they had worked themselves up into a fury. Hall Gudmundarson and Kálf Ásgeirsson were most insistent that they should get at Bolli and seek out Ósvíf's sons until they were found, for they could not possibly have gone anywhere outside the district, they said. But since Óláf was very set against this, peaceful negotiations were carried back and forth between the parties. This was easily taken care of with Bolli, for he asked Óláf to be sole arbitrator on his behalf. And as for Ósvíf, he saw no possible way out, for no help arrived from Snorri. A meeting for peaceful settlement was then arranged at Ljárskógar. Óláf was given free hand in the whole case. Any redress for the slaying of Kjartan was to be entirely Óláf's decision, both as to fines and outlawry. Then the peace parley broke up. Bolli had not come to the meeting; Óláf had seen to that. The penalties were to be made public at the Thórsnes Thing.

Afterwards the men from Mýrar and the Víddalers rode to Hjardarholt. Thorstein Kuggason offered to foster Ásgeir, Kjartan's son, as a comfort to Hrefna. She went north with her brothers, grieved and heavy of heart. But for all that she bore herself courteously, for she was mild and easy of speech with each and every one. Hrefna took no husband after Kjartan. She lived but a little while after going back north, and people say she died of a broken heart.

51

The Price of Peace

KJARTAN'S body lay in state at Hjardarholt for a week. Thorstein Egilsson had had a church built at Borg. He had Kjartan's body moved home with him, and Kjartan was buried at Borg. The church was newly consecrated and still draped in white.

Presently it was time for the Thórsnes Thing. The charges against

Ósvíf's sons were prepared and all of them were outlawed. They were granted enough money for their passage out of the country,[1] and they were not to return to Iceland so long as any of Óláf's sons were alive or Ásgeir Kjartansson. There was to be no wergild paid for Gudlaug, Ósvíf's nephew, on account of his part in the attack and ambush on Kjartan; nor was Thórólf to have any redress for the injury he had received. Óláf would not prosecute Bolli, but bade him put up compensation on his own behalf. Halldór and Steinthór were ill-content with that, as were Óláf's other sons, and they said it would prove hard for them to bear if Bolli were to remain in the same district with them. Óláf said that they would have to listen to him as long as he was alive.

There was a ship drawn up at Bjarnarhofn which belonged to Audun Festargarm (Bandog). He was at the Thing and was heard to say: "Chances are that these men will find themselves no less outlawed in Norway than here, if Kjartan's friends are still alive." Ósvíf called back: "You old tetherhound,[2] you, your words will never come true, for my sons will be honored by men of rank wherever they go, but you, Festargarm, will surely meet a bad end this summer." That summer Audun Festargarm put out to sea, and the ship was wrecked in the Faroe Islands. Every living soul on board perished. What Ósvíf had prophesied seemed very much to have come true.

Ósvíf's sons sailed out that summer, and not one of them ever came back. Thus the prosecution came to an end, with Óláf having gained in honor by it, for he had cut right to the core and done what was most meet and proper in the case of Ósvíf's sons, but had spared Bolli for kinship's sake. Óláf thanked the men for their support. Bolli got the land at Tunga on Óláf's authority.

It is said that Óláf lived three years after Kjartan was killed. Upon his death, his sons divided the inheritance he left. Halldór took over the farmstead at Hjardarholt, and Thorgerd, their mother, stayed with Halldór. She was deeply resentful toward Bolli and felt sorely repaid for her fostering.

CHART 18
The Relationship of Steinthór Óláfsson and Kjartan
to the House of Ásgeir Hothead

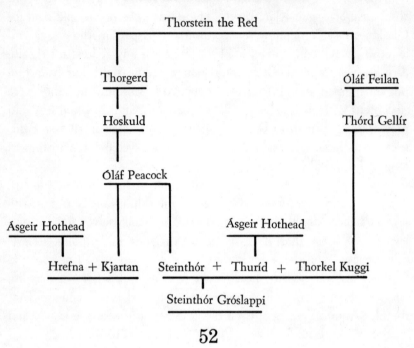

Thorstein the Red

Thorgerd   Óláf Feilan

Hoskuld   Thórd Gellír

Óláf Peacock

Ásgeir Hothead   Ásgeir Hothead

Hrefna + Kjartan   Steinthór + Thuríd + Thorkel Kuggi

Steinthór Gróslappi

52

A Reminder

BOLLI and Gudrún set up housekeeping in the spring at Saelings-dalstunga, and their farmstead soon came to be a stately one. A son was born to them, and the boy was given the name Thorleik. He soon developed into a fine lad and was very quick.

Halldór Óláfsson was living at Hjardarholt, as was told before. He was the foremost of those brothers. The same spring that Kjartan was killed, Thorgerd Egilsdóttir put a young lad, some kinsman of hers, into service with Thorkel of Hafratindar. The boy tended sheep there during the summer. For him as for many others Kjartan's death was the cause of great grief. The boy could never speak of Kjartan within Thorkel's hearing, for Thorkel always spoke ill of Kjartan, saying that he had been white-livered and fainthearted, and often mimicked how he had taken his death blow. The boy took this very hard and

went to Hjardarholt and told it to Halldór and Thorgerd and begged
them to take him in. Thorgerd told him to stay in Thorkel's service
until winter. The boy said he could not stand it there any longer —
"and you wouldn't ask me to if you knew how hard it was for me."
Then Thorgerd had a change of heart at his tale of woe and said as
far as she was concerned, he could have his way. Halldór said: "Don't
pay any attention to the lad; he's not worth taking so seriously."
Then Thorgerd answered: "The boy may not be worth much," she
said, "but Thorkel has conducted himself badly at every turn in this
affair. For he knew of the ambush the Laugar men laid for Kjartan
and didn't want to warn him, but got instead some fun and sport
for himself out of their exchange of blows, and since then he has
been making many nasty remarks. Far be it from you brothers ever
to seek out revenge when the odds are against you, if you can't even
pay back such a scoundrel as Thorkel for his part in this." Halldór
had little to say to that, but told Thorgerd to do as she thought best
about the boy's service.

A few days later Halldór and some other men rode off from home.
He went to Hafratindar and took Thorkel by surprise in his house,
led him out, and killed him; and Thorkel met his death like a
coward. This done, Halldór forbade any plundering and went home.
Thorgerd voiced her approval of the deed and thought this token
reminder better than none at all.

That summer everything was quiet, so to speak; but all the same,
relations between Bolli and Óláf's sons were most cool. The brothers
were as relentless toward Bolli as they could be. He, however, yielded
to his kinsmen in everything so long as he did not lose face by it, for
Bolli was not a man to be daunted. He had a large following and
lived in fine style, for there was no lack of money.

Steinthór Óláfsson lived at Donustadir in Laxárdal. He had Thuríd
Ásgeirsdóttir as a wife; she had been married to Thorkel Kuggi. Their
son was called Steinthór and had the nickname Gróslappi (Clumsy
Lubber).

53

Thorgerd's Prodding

TOWARD the end of the winter following Óláf Hoskuldsson's death, Thorgerd Egilsdóttir sent word to her son Steinthór that he should come to see her. And when mother and son met, she told him that she wanted to go west to Saurbaer to see her friend Aud. She told Halldór to come along too. He did so, and they made a party of five altogether. They kept on until they came opposite the farm at Saelingsdalstunga. There Thorgerd headed her horse up toward the farm and asked: "What farm is this?" Halldór answered: "You aren't asking this, mother, because you don't already know. This farm is called Tunga." "Who lives there?" she asked. He answered: "That you know too, mother." Then Thorgerd snorted: "I do indeed," she said, "there lives Bolli, your brother's slayer. You have certainly turned out very differently from your noble kinsmen, if you don't want to avenge such a brother as Kjartan was. Never would Egil, your mother's father, have acted this way. It's an ill thing to have shirkers for sons. Indeed, to my mind it would have suited you better had you been daughters to your father and married off. It just goes to prove the old saying — 'there's a black sheep in every family.' The way I see it, this was clearly Óláf's greatest misfortune: that he was cheated when it came to the kind of sons he got. I am telling this to you, Halldór, because you seem to be the foremost of your brothers. Now we shall turn back, for the sole purpose of my coming out here was just to remind you of this, in case you didn't remember it before." Then Halldór answered: "It certainly won't be any fault of yours, Mother, if we don't remember." Other than that Halldór had little to say about it, but all the same a fiery hate against Bolli welled up inside him.

The winter passed, summer came, and time for the Thing. Halldór let it be known that he was riding to the Thing, as did his brothers. They rode with a large company and fixed up the booth which Óláf had owned. The Thing was quiet and nothing to speak of happened. The Víddalers, the sons of Gudmund Solmundarson, came to the

Thing from the north. Bardi Gudmundarson was then eighteen years old; he was a big man and strong. Óláf's sons invited their kinsman Bardi home with them and strongly urged him to come. Hall Gudmundarson was not in the country at the time. Bardi was happy to accept, for these kinsmen were very fond of one another. So Bardi rode west from the Thing with Óláf's sons. They came home to Hjardarholt, and Bardi stayed on there for the rest of the summer.

54

Laying of Plans

HALLDÓR now told Bardi secretly that he and his brothers meant to go after Bolli, saying they could no longer stand their mother's taunts. "It is not to be denied, kinsman Bardi, that a great part of the reason we asked you home with us was because we wanted to have your backing in this." Bardi answered: "That will be sure to cause some nasty talk, this breaking faith with one's kinsmen, and besides Bolli to my mind is a hard one to get at. He has many men around him and is himself a very stalwart fellow. And there will be no lack of shrewd counsel with Gudrún and Ósvíf around. All in all it strikes me as no easy task." Halldór said: "There's no need to make this appear more difficult for us than it is. Nor did I bring this up before I knew that a try for revenge against Bolli could be carried out successfully. I daresay, kinsman, you won't refuse undertaking this with us." Bardi answered: "I know that it wouldn't seem right to you if I turned you down. And I will not do so either, if I see that I cannot keep you from it." "You have chosen the right thing," said Halldór, "as was to be expected." Bardi said they would have to go about it cautiously. Halldór said he had heard that Bolli had sent his men from home, some up to Hrútafjord to his ship, and some out along the strands. "I have also been told that Bolli is at the summer hut in Saelingsdal and that there are no men there, other than his housecarls who are doing the haying. As I see it, there could be no better time than now to try for an attack on Bolli." So they settled this between them, Halldór and Bardi.

CHART 19

Óláf's Sons Halldór and Steinthór and Their Cousin Bardi

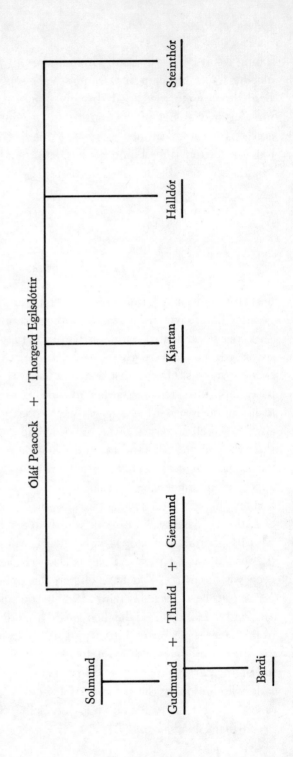

There was a man by the name of Thorstein the Black. He lived in Hundadal in the Breidafjord Dales, a wise man and well-to-do. He had been an old and good friend of Óláf Peacock. Thorstein had a sister called Sólveig; she was married to a man by the name of Helgi Hardbeinsson. Helgi was a big man and strong and was a great seafaring trader. He had just recently come out to Iceland and was staying with Thorstein, his brother-in-law. Halldór sent word to Thorstein the Black and to Helgi, his brother-in-law, to come to Hjardarholt; and when they came, Halldór told them his intentions and plan and asked them to join in the venture with them. But Thorstein voiced his disapproval of it: "It is a great pity that you kinsmen should continue killing one another off. There are few enough like Bolli left in your family as it is."

But even though Thorstein spoke that way, it was to no avail. Halldór sent word to Lambi, his father's half brother, and when he came, Halldór told of his plan. Lambi urged it very much and was eager for it to be carried out. Thorgerd, the mistress of the house, also did her share of egging them on. She said she would never feel Kjartan avenged unless Bolli paid with his life. And so they made ready to go.

On this trip there were the four brothers: Halldór and Steinthór, Helgi and Hoskuld; Bardi Gudmundarson was the fifth; Lambi was the sixth,[1] Thorstein the seventh; Helgi, his brother-in-law, the eighth; and Án Brushwood Belly the ninth. Thorgerd was set on going along with them. They tried to dissuade her by saying such ventures were not for women, but she said she was most certainly going to go — "for nobody knows better than I that you, my sons, need a prodding now and then." They said she could do as she wished.

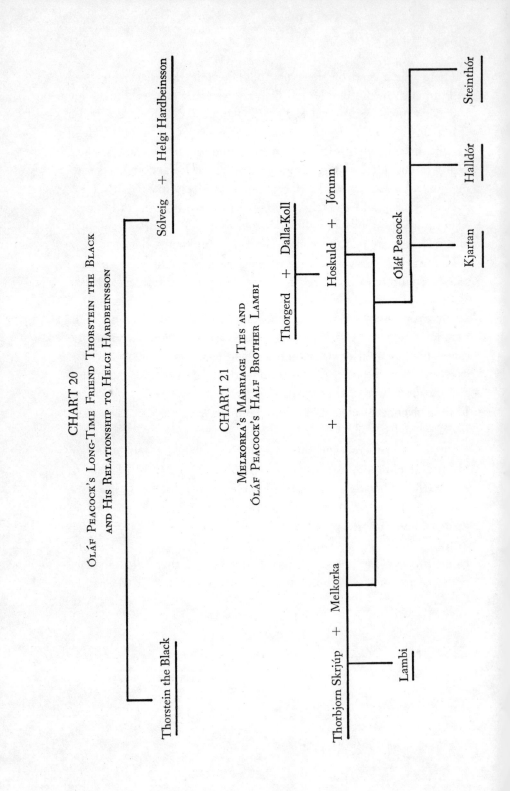

CHART 20

Óláf Peacock's Long-Time Friend Thorstein the Black and His Relationship to Helgi Hardbeinsson

Thorstein the Black

Sólveig + Helgi Hardbeinsson

CHART 21

Melkorka's Marriage Ties and Óláf Peacock's Half Brother Lambi

Thorbjorn Skrjúp + Melkorka

Lambi

+

Thorgerd + Dalla-Koll

Hoskuld + Jórunn

Óláf Peacock

Kjartan   Halldór   Steinthór

55

Evening the Score

THEY rode off out of Hjardarholt, the nine of them together. Thorgerd was the tenth. They rode in along the foreshore and so on to Ljárskógar. That was in the early part of the night. They made no stop until they came to Saelingsdal, arriving just before daybreak. There were thick woods in the valley at that time. Bolli was there at the shiel, just as Halldór had heard. The huts stood by the side of a river at that place which is now called Bollatoptir. A large wood stretched from above the shiel all the way down to Stakkagil. Between the slope and the wood there was a wide meadow called Barm. There Bolli's housecarls were doing the haying. Halldór and his company rode up to Oxnagróf, across the plains of Ránarvellir and thus down over the meadow at Hamarengi,[1] which is across from the shiel. They knew that some men were there, so they dismounted and planned to wait until they went off to work.

Bolli's shepherd went out early that morning to his cattle up on the slope. He caught sight of the men in the woods and also saw the horses which were tied. He guessed that these likely were no peaceable men who were keeping their travelings so secret, so he headed right for home, cutting straight across to the hut, in order to tell Bolli of the men's presence. Halldór had a sharp eye. He saw the man running down the slope and making straight for the hut. He told his companions it was probably Bolli's shepherd — "and he must have seen our party. We must now head him off and not let him bring any news to the hut."

They did as he suggested. Án Brushwood Belly rode the fastest and caught up with the boy, lifted him off his feet and flung him down. The boy fell in such a way that his back was broken. After that they rode to the shiel. There were two sheds, the sleeping hut and the storehouse. Bolli had been up and about early that morning getting the day's work allotted, but had lain down again to sleep after his housecarls went off to work. There were just two at the hut, Bolli and Gudrún. They woke up to the clatter of men dismounting from their horses, and heard them debating about who should be the first

to go in and get at Bolli. Bolli recognized Halldór by his voice and
some of the others. Bolli spoke with Gudrún and told her to get away
from the hut, saying that this meeting would be one she would get
little pleasure from. Gudrún replied that she did not think anything
would happen there which she could not stand to see, and added
that Bolli would not be the worse off for her staying there by him.
Bolli said he was the one to decide that, and so Gudrún went out
from the hut. She went down the slope to the brook which ran past
there and took to washing her linen. Bolli was now alone in the hut.
He took up his weapons, set his helmet on his head, and held his
shield before him. He had the sword Footbite in his hand, but had
on no coat of mail.

Halldór and his men were trying to make up their minds as to how
they ought to go about it, for no one was very eager to go in first.
Then Án Brushwood Belly spoke up: "There are men along here who
are more closely related to Kjartan than I am, but not one who bears
it more clearly in mind than I do what took place when Kjartan lost
his life. Even as I was carried back to Tunga, more dead than alive,
and Kjartan lay slain, the uppermost thought in my mind was that I
would only too gladly do some harm to Bolli if I got the chance. So
I'll be the first to go into the hut." Thorstein the Black answered:
"That is valiantly spoken but still it would be wiser not to rush head-
long into something without due thought; let us go at this cautiously,
for Bolli won't simply be standing quietly by when he's being attacked. Now even if he is caught shorthanded, you can expect a stiff
fight on his part, for Bolli is both strong and skilled in arms. And
that sword of his is a trusty one as weapons go."

Presently Án made a determined dash into the hut, holding his
shield over his head with the narrow end forward. Bolli struck at him
with Footbite, shearing off the tail end of the shield and cleaving
Án's skull in two, right down to the shoulders. That was Án's death
blow, needless to say.[2] Then in went Lambi holding his shield in
front of him and his sword drawn in his hand. At just that moment
Bolli was drawing Footbite out of Án's wound, and in so doing
Bolli's shield shifted over to one side, leaving him open to attack.
Lambi then laid on a blow at Bolli's thigh, and that was a big wound.
Bolli struck back at Lambi's shoulder and ran his sword down the

length of his side. That put Lambi out of the fight forthwith, and
never did he have use of his arm again as long as he lived. At that
moment Helgi Hardbeinsson went in with a spear in his hand that
had a blade one ell long and its shaft wound with iron. And when
Bolli saw that, he threw down his sword, took hold of his shield
firmly with both hands and went toward the door of the hut to meet
Helgi head on. But Helgi lunged at Bolli with his spear, running it
right through the shield and Bolli himself. Bolli leaned back up
against the wall of the hut. Now the rest of them crowded inside —
Halldór and his brothers. Thorgerd went in too.

Then Bolli spoke: "Now it's safe for you to come closer, brothers,"
and said he imagined it would be but a short defense. It was Thorgerd who gave answer to him, saying there was no call for not making sure that Bolli was completely done for, and bade them smite
him a blow between the head and the trunk. Bolli was still standing
up against the wall of the hut holding his kirtle tight to him to keep
his viscera from running out. Then Steinthór Óláfsson leapt at Bolli
and struck him a blow with a great axe at the base of the neck and
his head flew off. Thorgerd wished him "all hale" to enjoy the fruits
of his labor and said that Gudrún would have something to busy
herself with for a while — combing Bolli's bloody locks.

After that they went out of the hut. Gudrún then came up from
the brook and walked over to talk to Halldór and the others and
asked what had taken place in their dealings with Bolli. They told
her just the way it had happened. Gudrún was wearing a kirtle of
foreign mode with a tight-fitting bodice of fine wool and had a high
bent coif on her head. She had tied a shawl around her, embroidered
in blue and with fringe on the ends. Helgi Hardbeinsson went up
to Gudrún and took the end of her shawl and wiped the blood off his
spear, the very one with which he had made the thrust through Bolli.
Gudrún looked up at him and smiled. Then Halldór spoke up: "That
is a mean and cruel thing to do." Helgi told him not to let it bother
him — "for I daresay," he said, "that under this scarf end is nurtured
the bane of my life."

With that they took to their horses and rode away. Gudrún went
a piece with them, talking with them the while. Then she turned
back.

56

Biding Time

TALK STARTED up among Halldór's men about how little to heart Gudrún seemed to take Bolli's death, seeing how she chatted along the way with them, as if they had done nothing against her. Halldór spoke up: "It's not my feeling that Gudrún takes Bolli's loss little to heart. I think this chatting along the way of hers was more to make sure just exactly what men were in on this raid. It certainly isn't going too far to say that Gudrún is way beyond most women in character. So it is no more than to be expected that she will take Bolli's loss very much to heart. If the truth be told, it is a great pity to lose such a man as Bolli, even if we kinsmen didn't have the good fortune to get along together." And so they rode home to Hjardarholt.

It did not take long for this news to spread far and wide, and it was thought grave. Bolli's death was cause for great grief. Gudrún sent men at once to Snorri Godi, for she and Ósvíf felt they could always rely on complete support where Snorri was concerned. He was quick to respond to Gudrún's message and came on to Tunga sixty men strong. Gudrún was happy that he came. He offered to try for a peaceful settlement, but Gudrún was little minded to agree to accepting payment for Bolli's slaying on behalf of her son Thorleik. "As far as I can see you can best help me out, Snorri, if you would change dwelling places with me so that I don't have to be sitting right next door to the Hjardholters." At that time Snorri himself was having serious quarrels with the people of Eyr,[1] so he said he would do that for Gudrún, for friendship's sake — "but you will have to stay on at Tunga this winter." Snorri now got ready to leave and Gudrún gave him fine gifts. And so Snorri rode home, and it was quiet the rest of the year, so to speak.

The winter following Bolli's slaying, Gudrún gave birth to a child; it was a boy, and he was named Bolli. He soon grew into a big and fine boy, and Gudrún loved him very much. When that winter drew to a close and spring came, Snorri and Gudrún made a trade of their lands, just as they had bargained. Snorri moved to Tunga and dwelt there for the rest of his life. Gudrún went to Helgafell, and there

she and Ósvíf set up a splendid household. There Gudrún's sons grew
up, Thorleik and Bolli. Thorleik was four years old at the time his
father Bolli was killed.

57

Of Thorgils Holluson and Thorkel Eyjólfsson

THERE was a man by the name of Thorgils Holluson; he was Halla's
son and was named after his mother because she lived longer than
his father. His father was Snorri, the son of Álf of the Dales. Halla,
Thorgils' mother, was Gest Oddleifsson's daughter. Thorgils lived
in Hordadal at the farm called Tunga. He was a big, handsome man,
but a swaggerer and known for being unfair and hard to deal with.
Often relations were rather cool between him and Snorri Godi, for
Snorri thought Thorgils meddlesome and puffed up. Thorgils found
all sorts of excuses for errands out in the district and was always
coming to Helgafell and offering to be of help to Gudrún in any
way he could. She took this in good part on the one hand, but on
the whole committed herself neither one way nor the other. Thorgils
offered to take her son Thorleik home with him, and Thorleik was
at Tunga for a long time and studied law with Thorgils, for he was
very well versed in the law.

At that time Thorkel Eyjólfsson was out traveling and trading
abroad. He was a well-known man, of high birth, and a great friend
of Snorri Godi. He usually stayed with his kinsman Thorstein
Kuggason whenever he was out in Iceland. One time when Thorkel
had his ship lying up at Vadil on the Bardastrond, it happened that
the son of Eid from Ás was killed in Borgarfjord by the sons of
Helga from Kropp. Grím was the name of the one who had done
the killing, and his brother's name was Njál. Njál drowned shortly
after in the Hvítá. Grím was sentenced and outlawed for the killing,
and he hid out in the mountains while he was under outlawry. He
was a big man and strong.

Eid was already a very old man when this happened and for that
reason no action was taken to prosecute the case. But Thorkel Eyjólfs-

son always had people hounding him because he had not set matters straight. The following spring, as soon as Thorkel had his ship ready, he sailed south across the Breidafjord. There he got himself a horse and rode off alone, not stopping until he came to this kinsman Eid at Ás. Eid was very happy to see him. Thorkel told him he had come because he wanted to seek out Grím, the outlaw, and asked Eid if he knew where he might be hiding out. Eid answered: "I'm not very keen about this, for I think you are taking a big chance on how this venture will turn out for you, especially when you're dealing with such a hellhound as Grím. But if you are bent on going, take some more men along so that you have the situation in hand." "There's no fame or gain, it seems to me, in taking unfair advantage of one man," said Thorkel, "but I would like it if you would lend me your sword Skofnung, for I imagine I can ward off one lone vagabond then, no matter how able-bodied he may be." "You'll have to suit yourself," said Eid, "but it won't surprise me if some time or other you come to regret this wilful action of yours. However, since you are thinking of doing this for my sake, I shall not refuse you your request, for I will feel Skofnung has come into good hands if you have it. The nature of this sword is such, though, that the sun must not shine on the hilt and it must not be drawn in the presence of women.[1] If a man gets a wound from this sword, it will never mend unless the healing stone that belongs with the sword is rubbed on it." Thorkel said he would keep this well in mind and took the sword. He asked Eid to point out the direction in which Grím might have his hideout. Eid said he rather expected that Grím would be hiding out up north around Tvídaegra near the Fiskivotn.[2] Then Thorkel rode north along the heath taking the road which Eid had indicated to him, and when he had gone a long way over the heath, he spied a hut by a large lake, and headed over that way.

CHART 22

The Lineage of Thorgils Holluson and Thorkel Eyjólfsson from the Two Sides of Ketil's House

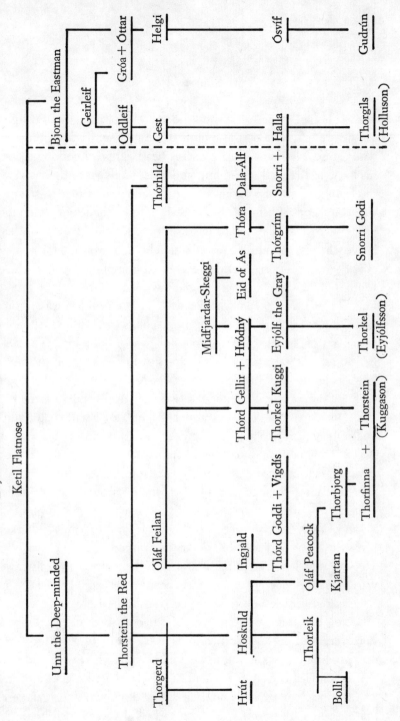

58

Snorri's Wiles

Now Thorkel came to the hut and saw that a man was sitting down by the water's edge at the mouth of a brook and was pulling in fish with a line. He had a cloak over his head. Thorkel got down and tied his horse at the wall of the hut, and went on down to the water where the man was sitting. Grím saw the shadow of a man cast onto the water and quickly started to his feet. Thorkel had by that time come up very close to him and struck at him. The blow landed on his arm above the wrist, but it was not much of a wound. Grím made a quick leap at Thorkel, and they fell to grappling. Soon the odds in strength told, and Thorkel went down with Grím right on top of him. Then Grím asked who he was. Thorkel said it was no matter. Grím said: "Things no doubt have come to a different pass from what you expected, for now your life is in my hands." Thorkel said he would not beg for mercy — "for my luck has gone against me." Grím said he had had enough of misfortunes so that he could do without this one — "Another fate is in all likelihood in store for you other than dying at this encounter of ours. So I will spare your life, and you may repay me in whatever way you wish."

With this both of them got up and went back to the hut. Thorkel noticed that Grím was growing weak from loss of blood. So he took the Skofnung stone and rubbed it on the wound and bound it to Grím's arm, and it at once took all the smart and swelling out of the wound. They stayed there overnight. In the morning Thorkel got ready to leave and asked Grím if he wanted to go along with him. He said that he most certainly did. Thorkel turned straightway westward and did not go to see Eid, nor did he stop until he came to Saelingsdalstunga. Snorri Godi received him with a hearty welcome. Thorkel told him that his venture had turned out badly. Snorri, however, said it had turned out well — "and luckily for Grím, it appears to me. I want you to do well by him when you send him off. But my advice to you, my friend, would be that you give up traveling and trading, get yourself married and settle down and make a chieftain of yourself, as you were born to be." Thorkel answered: "Many a time your advice has stood me in good stead," and then asked whether Snorri had given it any thought as to what woman he should ask. Snorri answered: "You are to ask that one woman who is the best match to be had and that is Gudrún Ósvífsdóttir." Thorkel said it was quite true that the match was a worthy one — "but I have my grave doubts when it comes to her headstrong temper," he said, "and her ambitious plans. She will want to have her husband Bolli avenged, and Thorgils Holluson seems to be in on that with her, so all this may not be altogether to his liking. But Gudrún otherwise suits me fine." Snorri said: "I shall see to it that Thorgils won't cause you any trouble. And it seems more than likely to me that events will take a turn, as far as revenge for Bolli is concerned, before this season is out." Thorkel answered: "It may well be that you aren't just making empty talk. But as for revenge for Bolli, I don't see any more likelihood of that now than before, unless of course some bigger men are drawn into a plan."[1] Snorri replied: "I would like you to go abroad once more this summer; let's see then how things go." Thorkel agreed, and with this settled, they parted company.

Thorkel went off to the west across the Breidafjord country and to his ship. He took Grím abroad with him. They had good weather that summer and made Norway somewhat to the south. Then Thorkel said to Grím: "It is well known to you what events led up to our coming together, so there's no need to go into that. But I would very much like it to end more pleasantly than was foreseeable a while back. I have found you to be a stalwart fellow and for that reason I want to send you off as though I had never borne you any ill will. I will supply you with enough trading goods so that you can easily join the ranks of valiant merchants, but do not settle down here in the north of the country, for there are many of Eid's kinsmen on trading journeys hereabouts who still bear you ill will." Grím thanked him for these words and said he never would have dreamed of asking for as much as Thorkel was offering. At parting Thorkel gave Grím a liberal amount of trading goods. Many remarked that Thorkel had acted most nobly. After that Grím went east to Vík and settled down there. He was looked on as a man of much account, and herewith ends all there is to say of Grím.

Thorkel stayed in Norway over the winter and was thought a man of great importance. He had a wealth of goods and was an ambitious fellow.

Now let us turn our attention away from this for a while and take up the story out in Iceland and see what went on there while Thorkel was abroad.

59

A Twist

GUDRÚN Ósvífsdóttir set out from home that summer in the double month and went to the Dales. She rode to Thykkvaskóg. Thorleik was then staying in turns with Ármód's sons, Halldór and Ornólf, at Thykkvaskóg and with Thorgils at Tunga. That same evening Gudrún sent a man to Snorri Godi to tell him that she wanted to see him the very next day. Snorri was quick to respond and rode at once with one other man until he came to the Haukadalsá. A crag juts out on the north side of the river and is called Hofdi.[1] It is on land belonging to Laekjarskóg. At this place Gudrún had said she and Snorri were to meet. They both arrived at almost the same time. One other also came with Gudrún; that was Bolli Bollason. He was then twelve years old, but just as mature in body and mind as many were after they had reached full manhood. He was also carrying Footbite.

Snorri and Gudrún fell to talking at once, but Bolli sat up on the crag with Snorri's companion and watched the comings and goings of people about the district. And when Snorri and Gudrún had finished their exchange of general news, Snorri asked Gudrún what business she had and if something had recently come up to make her send him word in such a hurry. Gudrún answered: "It is true that for me this event which I am about to bring up is as brand new as though it happened yesterday, but it took place all the same twelve years ago. It is vengeance for Bolli that I will speak of. That ought not to come as any great surprise, for I have reminded you of it from time to time. I will also remind you that you have promised me some assistance if I would only wait patiently, but now there doesn't seem to be any hope of your heeding our agreement. I have now waited as long a time as I've a mind to, but still I would like to have sound advice from you as to where vengeance is to strike."

Snorri asked in what direction her thoughts were running. Gudrún said: "I am determined that Óláf's sons should not come out of this unscathed." Snorri said he would put a stop to any attack on those men who counted for most in the district — "and who are near kin to those who will go far when it comes to revenge. And besides it is high time that these family feuds come to an end." Gudrún said "Then Lambi shall be attacked and slain. At least that gets rid of the evilest of them." Snorri answered: "There is reason enough that Lambi be killed, but it doesn't seem to me that this will avenge Bolli either, for in the peace terms there will be no account taken of the disparity between Lambi and Bolli, if one weighs these two killings one against the other." Gudrún said: "It may well be that we can't even the score exactly with these Laxdalers, but now someone or other must pay dearly, no matter from what dale he comes. So now let's turn to Thorstein the Black, for no one has dealt himself a worse share in this affair than he." Snorri said: "Thorstein is neither more nor less guilty than any of those men who were in on Bolli's killing but didn't actually lay hands on him. But it seems to me you are letting those sit quietly by where revenge would be more in order — those who have actually brought about Bolli's death, for instance, Helgi Hardbeinsson." Gudrún said: "That's true, but I can't stand seeing those men against whom I have been nurturing my hate all along left to sit in peace." Snorri answered: "Then I have sound advice. Lambi and Thorstein are to join up with your sons; for the two of them that is a more than fair price for peace. But if they are unwilling, then I won't make any more excuses to keep you from fashioning whatever punishment you like for them." Gudrún asked: "How is one to persuade these men you have mentioned to join in?" Snorri said: "That's up to those who are to head the venture." Gudrún said: "I'm sure we can count on your good judgment to suggest the right one to lead and direct the undertaking." Then Snorri smiled and said: "You have already chosen the man for it." Gudrún replied: "You no doubt mean Thorgils." Snorri said she was right. Gudrún said: "I have discussed this with Thorgils before, but that seems to be as far as it can go, for he stipulated that one thing which I didn't care to consider: he agreed to avenge Bolli only if he got to marry me. And there's little hope of that, so I can't ask him to join in the raid." Snorri said: "I'll give you a piece of advice. By all means promise marriage to Thorgils, but with the underhand stipulation that you will not marry any countryman now here in Iceland except Thorgils;[1] and that will work, for Thorkel Eyjólfsson is not here in the country right now, and I have been intending this marriage for him." Gudrún said: "He is sure to see through that twist." Snorri answered: "I'm sure he won't, for Thorgils is better known for his impulsiveness than his sharp wit. Make this bargain in the presence of but few witnesses; you can let his foster brother Halldór be present but not Ornólf, for he is more quick-witted, and if it doesn't work, let me know."

After that he and Gudrún ended their talk and bade each other farewell. Snorri rode home and Gudrún went back to Thykkvaskóg. The following morning Gudrún rode from Thykkvaskóg together with her sons. And as they were riding out along the Skógarstrond they noticed that somebody was riding after them. Whoever it was, was riding at a sharp pace and soon caught up: it was none other than Thorgils Holluson. They gave one another a warm greeting and rode all together on out to Helgafell that day.

60

Gudrún's Prodding

A FEW days after Gudrún had come home, she called her sons for a talk in her leek garden.[1] And when they got there, they saw spread out on the ground linen clothes, a shirt and breeches. They were all stained with blood. Then Gudrún said: "These same clothes that you see here cry out to the two of you for the revenge of your father. Now I'm not going to waste my breath on this, for there's not much hope of your being whetted by words, if such tokens and reminders do not impress it on your minds." The brothers were very much moved by what Gudrún said, but all the same gave the answer that they had been too young to carry out revenge and were leaderless. They said that they had not been in a position to devise a plan for themselves, let alone others — "but still we might be able to remember what our loss has been." Gudrún said she suspected they had been thinking more about horse fights or sports. After this they walked away.

That night the brothers could not sleep. Thorgils noticed this and asked them what was the matter. They told him everything that had been said between them and their mother and added that they could no longer bear their own grief or their mother's taunts. "We want to seek out revenge," said Bolli, "and we brothers have now reached that age and maturity when people will strongly censure us if we don't lift a hand."

The next day Thorgils and Gudrún took up a conversation with one another and Gudrún started off by saying: "I am given to believe, Thorgils, that my sons are no longer content with sitting around quietly and doing nothing about revenge for their father. But the main reason for the delay has been that Thorleik and Bolli have seemed too young to me to take part in such plots. Yet there's no denying that something should have been considered long before this." Thorgils answered: "There is no point in your discussing this matter with me, seeing that you have taken so contrarily to marrying me. And I'm in just the same frame of mind as before when we talked this over. If I get to marry you, I won't blench at anything, be it finishing off one or both of them who had the most to do with Bolli's killing." Gudrún said: "I'm sure Thorleik feels there's no one equally as well suited to be leader as you, especially where the job to be done requires some courage. However, I will not keep it from you that my sons are planning to go after Helgi Hardbeinsson, that berserker who is sitting in Skorradal on his farm without the slightest misgivings." Thorgils said: "He can be called Helgi or anything whatever for all I care. I don't think Helgi or anyone else will be too much of a match for me. Enough has been said about this, as far as I'm concerned, provided you promise with witnesses to marry me if I carry out this revenge together with your sons." Gudrún said she would fulfill everything which she might have to agree to, even if it were done in the presence of only a few witnesses, and that it should be so settled. Gudrún asked to have his foster brother Halldór present and also her sons. Thorgils requested that Ornólf also be there. Gudrún said there was no need of that — "I have more doubts about Ornólf's faithfulness to you than you yourself seem to have." Thorgils said it was up to her.

Now the brothers came together with Gudrún and Thorgils, and Halldór was in on the talk with them. Gudrún now explained to them: "Thorgils has promised to be the leader in a raid on Helgi Hardbeinsson together with my sons to avenge Bolli. Furthermore Thorgils has made it a condition for his taking part in the raid that he get my hand in marriage. Now with you as witnesses, I hereby testify and promise not to marry any other countryman in the land except Thorgils. And I do not intend to get married in another land." To Thorgils it seemed that this ought to be binding enough, and he did not see through it. They ended the parley, and the decision was carried through that Thorgils was to undertake the raid. He set out from Helgafell together with Gudrún's sons. They rode in through the Dales and first home to Tunga.

61

Hard Choices

THE NEXT Lord's day there was a local Thing, and Thorgils rode to it with his following. Snorri Godi was not there, but it was well attended. During the day Thorgils asked Thorstein the Black for a talk and said: "It so happens, as you well know, that you were in on the raid with Óláf's sons at the time when Bolli was killed. You have as yet made no amends for this with Bolli's sons. Now even though much time has passed since these events took place, I don't imagine they have forgotten just what men were in on the raid. Now then, the brothers are of the opinion that it would be least fitting for them to go after Óláf's sons because of their kinship; so they plan to turn their revenge on Helgi Hardbeinsson, who dealt Bolli his death wound. We would like you, Thorstein, to be in on this raid with the brothers and thus buy your way to peace and pardon." Thorstein answered: "It is not at all right for me to be party to a plot against my brother-in-law Helgi. I would much rather give payment for my peace, as much as would seem right and honorable." Thorgils said: "I scarcely imagine that the brothers will turn this into a money-making proposition for themselves. You might as well face the facts, Thorstein, that you have two choices before you: either you decide to go along or take the consequences as soon as Bolli's sons get a chance. I myself would like to see you make the first choice, even if you are under obligation to Helgi. When one gets into such a pinch, one has to look out for himself." Thorstein said: "Will the same choice be given to any of the others who are involved in these charges?" Thorgils answered: "Lambi will also have to make the same choice." Thorstein said he would feel better about it if he did not have to be in on it alone.

After that Thorgils called in Lambi for a talk and told Thorstein to stay and listen. He said: "I want to discuss the same matter with you, Lambi, that I have brought up with Thorstein. What sort of redress are you willing to offer Bolli's sons for the charges they have against you? For we know for a fact that you dealt Bolli an injury. The fact that you are all the more guilt-laden, because you urged that Bolli be slain, is offset by the fact that next to Óláf's sons you had all the more reason for it." Lambi asked what would be demanded of him. Thorgils answered that the same choice would be given to him as to Thorstein, to join up with the brothers in the attack. Lambi said: "It's an ill price to pay for peace, and unmanly besides. I'm not at all keen on this undertaking." Then Thorstein spoke: "It's not all that simple, Lambi, just to turn your back on joining in, for those who are involved are men of weight and feel that they have been holding the short end long enough. Bolli's sons are promising men, full of pluck and ambition, so I'm told, and they have cause enough to take revenge. We can hardly do less than to try to redeem ourselves to some extent after such a gross deed. People are also likely to put the blame mostly on me because of the kinship between myself and Helgi, and besides it seems to me self-evident that most people would rather sacrifice anything but life itself. That trouble must be pushed aside first which presses the hardest." Lambi spoke up: "It's easy to hear what you're desirous of, Thorstein. I think it best that you have the say in this, seeing that you think it's all so simple, for we have long been partners through thick and thin, you and I. But I want to make this stipulation: if I do go along and if the revenge against Helgi is successful, my kinsmen, Óláf's sons, must be left alone and in peace." Thorgils agreed to this on behalf of the brothers.

It was decided, then, that Thorstein and Lambi were to join up with Thorgils on the raid. They made the agreement that they should all meet at Tunga in Hordadal three days hence, early in the morning. After that they parted. Thorgils rode home that evening to Tunga. The time was now at hand when those who planned to go with Thorgils on the raid should come to meet him. Before sunup on the morning of the third day, Thorstein and Lambi arrived at Tunga. Thorgils gave them good welcome.

62

Smelling Out the Fox

THORGILS now prepared to leave. They rode up along Hordadal, ten together. Thorgils Holluson was the leader of the band. In his troop were Bolli's sons, Bolli and Thorleik, and their half brother Thórd Cat made the fourth. The fifth was Thorstein the Black, the sixth Lambi; Halldór and Ornólf made the seventh and eighth, Svein the ninth and Húnbogi the tenth. These two were the sons of Álf of the Dales. All of them were stalwart fighters. They took the road up to Sópandaskard and across Langavatnsdal and cut across the Borgarfjord country. They rode up to Eyjárvad and forded the Nordrá and on to Bakkavad where they forded the Hvitá a short distance downstream from Baer. Then they rode up Reykjadal, across the ridge into Skorradal, and so up along the woods in the neighborhood of the farm at Vatnshorn. There they got down from their horses. It was then well along into the evening. The farm at Vatnshorn stood a short way from the water on the south side of the river. Thorgils told his companions they would stay there overnight. "And I will go over to the farm and scout around to find out whether Helgi is at home. I've been told that he usually has rather few people about but is extremely wary when it comes to his own person, and that he sleeps in a sturdy bedcloset." Thorgils' companions told him to go and have a look around.

Thorgils now makes a change of clothes, taking off his blue hooded cloak and putting on a gray rain cloak. He goes off in the direction of the farm, and when he had come nearly up to the fence, he sees a man walking toward him, and when they come up to one another, Thorgils says: "You will think I am asking a foolish question, my friend, but where have I come to in the district and what farm is this, and who lives here?" The man answered: "You must be terribly stupid if you haven't heard of Helgi Hardbeinsson, the bravest and boldest warrior and chieftain." Thorgils then asked how lenient Helgi was when it came to taking people in, should strangers come to him who were in much need of help. The man answered: "There is truly only good to be said for Helgi, for he is a great and generous man both when it comes to taking people in and doing other good deeds." "Is Helgi at home now?" asked Thorgils. "I would like to try out his hospitality." The other asked what sort of trouble he was in. Thorgils answered: "I was outlawed last summer at the Thing. I wanted now to seek support from this man who is supposed to be such a grand fellow. In return I would give him my help and service. So now take me up to the farmhouse to find Helgi." "Bring you up to the house I certainly can," the man said, "and lodging for the night will be at your disposal; but you won't find Helgi, for he is not at home." Then Thorgils asked where he was. The man answered: "Helgi is up at his summer hut at that place called Sarp." Thorgils asked where that was and what men were with him. The man said his son Hardbein was there and two others who were outlaws, whom Helgi had taken in. Thorgils asked him to show him the quickest and shortest way to the hut, "for I want to meet him as soon as I can, and get my errand over with."

The house servant obliged by showing him the way, and after that they parted. Thorgils turned back into the woods and to his companions and told them what he had found out about Helgi's whereabouts and doings. "We will stay here through the night and not go on to the hut until tomorrow." They did as he said. In the morning

Thorgils and his party rode up along the woods until they came a
short distance from the hut. There Thorgils told them to dismount
and eat their morning meal. They did so and tarried there a while.

63

The Circle in the Woods

BUT NOW let us see what is going on at the hut where Helgi was,
together with those men we mentioned before. That morning Helgi
told his shepherd to make the rounds in the woods in the neighborhood of the shiel and to be on the lookout for any comings or goings,
or anything else he might see worth reporting — "for I have had some
bad dreams in the night," he added. The boy did what he was told.
He was gone for a while and when he came back, Helgi asked
whether he had seen anything worth telling. He answered: "I have
seen something which I think will be news." Helgi asked what that
was. He said he had seen some men, not all too few either — "and I
think they are likely to have come from outside the district." Helgi
asked: "Where were they when you saw them, and what were they
up to, and did you notice anything special about what they had on
or what they looked like?" He answered: "I didn't get so badly
frightened that I didn't take time to notice that, for I knew you
would ask it." He went on to say that they were a short distance
from the hut and were eating their morning meal. Helgi asked
whether they were sitting in a ring or each one off by himself. The
boy said they were sitting in a ring on their saddles. Helgi said: "Now
tell me what they looked like. I want to see if I can guess from their
appearance who they might be." The lad said: "There was one man
sitting there on a brightly stained saddle with a blue hooded cloak on.
He was a big and bold-looking fellow, bald at the temples and somewhat buck-toothed." Helgi said: "That man I recognize easily from
your description. You have seen Thorgils Holluson from out west in
Hordadal. But what can that big bully want with us?"

The boy went on: "Next to him sat a man on a gilded saddle. He
was in a red-scarlet kirtle and wore a gold arm ring and had a gold

band tied around his head. This man had flaxen hair and it fell in curls down to his shoulders. He was of fair complexion, had a bump on his nose, which was turned up slightly on the end, very fine blue eyes, sharp and somewhat roving, a broad forehead and full cheeks. He had his hair cut straight across the brow, and was well developed in the shoulders and chest. He had fine hands and a strong wrist. His whole bearing was chivalrous, and all in all I can say that I have never seen any man equally as gallant. He was also such a young man that he had grown no hair on his upper lip. It seemed to me as though he might be full of grief."

Then Helgi answered: "You have certainly looked this man over very carefully. He no doubt must be of much account, but I don't believe I've ever seen him. So I'll make a guess as to who he is; I think it must have been Bolli Bollason, for I've been told that he is a man of promise."

Then the boy continued: "Then there was a man sitting on a saddle with enamel work. He was in a yellowish-green kirtle. He had on a large gold arm ring. This man was most handsome looking, and seemed young in years, had reddish-brown hair which was very comely, and all in all he was a most chivalrous youth." Helgi answered: "I think I know the man you have just described. That is no doubt Thorleik Bollason. But what a smart and sharp-sighted fellow you are!"

The boy continued: "Next to him sat a young man. He was in a blue kirtle and black breeches with his kirtle belted in. This man had regular features, light-colored hair and a pleasing face. He was of slight build and chivalrous." Helgi answered: "This man I recognize; I must have seen him just once, and he would have been very young at the time. That must be Thórd Thórdarson, Snorri Godi's foster son. But what a chivalrous lot these Westfirthers have along! What more is there then?"

Then the boy said: "Next there was a man sitting in a Scottish saddle; he had a hoary beard and swarthy complexion, and black, wiry hair, and was rather ugly to look at, but for all that seemed to be a doughty fellow. He had on a hooded cloak with pleats." Helgi said: "I can easily tell who that is. That's Lambi Thorbjarnarson from Laxárdal. But I don't see why he is along with the two brothers."

The boy went on: "Next there was a man sitting on a pommeled saddle and he wore a blue hooded cloak outermost and had a silver arm ring on. He had the look of a peasant, was rather past the prime of youth, and had dark auburn hair that was very curly. He had a scar on his face." "Now what you're telling me is getting worse," said Helgi, "for there you have probably seen my brother-in-law Thorstein the Black, and it certainly seems strange to me that he is along, for I would never think of making such a raid on him. But what more is there?"

He answered: "Then there were two other men sitting there. They looked alike and could have been middle-aged and were most stout and hardy looking, red-haired and freckle-faced but still good looking." Helgi said: "I can easily tell who those men are. They are Ármóð's sons, Halldór and Ornólf, Thorgils' foster brothers. What a discerning fellow you are! But now have you accounted for all the men you saw?"

He answered: "Very little now can I add to this. Next to these two there sat a man facing out of the circle. He had on a coat of plate mail and a steel helmet on his head with a brim on it, a hand's breadth wide. He had a shiny axe over his shoulder and the edge of it must have been an ell long. This man was dark-complexioned and dark-eyed and most viking-like." Helgi answered: "That man I can easily recognize from your description. That was Húnbogi the Strong, the son of Álf of the Dales. But it's hard for me to figure out what they are after. They certainly do have a select company for this venture."

The boy went on: "And there sat yet another man next to this strong-looking fellow. He had dark-brown hair, was chubby-faced and ruddy-complexioned, had bushy eyebrows and was a bit over medium height." Helgi said: "You don't need to say anything more; that was Svein, the son of Álf of the Dales, Húnbogi's brother. But we had better not be caught napping by these men, for if I don't miss my guess, they will want to get at me before they quit the district, and there are men in this party who would have called our encounter due, had it come somewhat earlier. Now those women who are here at the hut are to get into men's clothes and take the horses which are here by the hut and ride as quickly as possible to the winter quarters.

Maybe those who are lying in ambush so close by won't notice whether it is men or women riding away. All they need to do is give us a little time so that we can get men to us, and then there's no telling which of us has the better chance." The women rode away, four of them together.

Thorgils had a suspicion that news of them might have got through to Helgi, and he ordered his men to take to their horses and ride on the charge as fast as they could, which they did. But before they had mounted, a man came riding right toward them in plain sight. He was small of stature, lively and brisk with very darting eyes. He had a quick and responsive horse. This man greeted Thorgils like an old friend. Thorgils asked him his name and kin and also where he had come from. He said his name was Hrapp and that he was a Breid-firther on his mother's side — "and there I grew up. I bear the name Víga-Hrapp and have all that the name implies, for I am no easy man to deal with, even if I am undersized. I'm from the Southern Quarter on my father's side and have been staying there now for some years. But what a fine stroke of luck it is, Thorgils, that I have come on you here, for I was intending to go and see you anyway, even though that would have posed more or less of a problem for me, for I am in trouble. I've had a falling out with my master. I got some hard treatment from him, but I don't have my name for nothing. I'm not willing to take abuses from anybody, so I struck him. I guess it did little or nothing at all to him, but I didn't stay long enough to find out, for I felt safer as soon as I got on the back of this horse, which I stole from him." Hrapp did a lot of talking, but asked few questions; yet he found out soon enough that they were aiming to set on Helgi, and he voiced his approval of it and said that they wouldn't have to look around in the rear for him.

64

Helgi Hardbeinsson's Bane

THORGILS and his men set off at a fast pace, as soon as they got on
their horses, and rode forth out of the woods. They caught sight of
four men riding away from the shed; they too were riding at full
gallop. Then some of Thorgils' companions spoke up and said that
they should ride after them as fast as they could. Thorleik Bollason
answered: "Let us first get to the hut and find out who is there. For
I rather doubt that Helgi and his followers are in that group. It looks
to me as though they are only women." Most of the men argued
against him. Thorgils said Thorleik should decide, for he knew that
Thorleik was uncommonly sharp-sighted. They now headed for the
hut. Hrapp darted out ahead, brandishing the little stick of a spear
which he carried, thrusting it out in front of him, saying it was now
high time for him to prove himself.

Before Helgi and those with him were aware of it, Thorgils and
his men had the hut surrounded. Helgi and those inside barred the
doors and took up their weapons. Hrapp jumped right up onto the
hut roof and asked whether the fox was at home. Helgi answered:
"You'll soon find out that he who lives inside is a bit ugly and knows
how to bite if anyone gets too near his lair." And with that Helgi
thrust his spear through the roof opening and straight through Hrapp.
He fell back off the spear and down to the ground dead. Thorgils
told the others to go cautiously and be on their guard against needless
mishaps — "for we have force enough to take the hut and Helgi, the
fix he has got himself into now, for I have an idea that there are
but few men inside."

The hut was built with one main ridgepole which rested on the
gables and stuck out beyond them, and the sod thatch on the house
was only in a single layer and was not yet grown over with grass.
Then Thorgils told some of the men to take hold of the ends of the
ridgepole and pull down on it so hard that it either broke or the
rafters sagged in. Others he told to guard the door in case anyone
tried to get out. There were five in the hut counting Helgi. His son
Hardbein was there — he was then twelve years old — and his shep-

herd lad and two other men who had come to him that summer and were under outlawry; the one was called Thorgils and the other Eyjólf.

Thorstein the Black stood before the door of the hut together with Svein, the son of Álf of the Dales, while the others were riving off the roof. They had divided up for the work. Húnbogi the Strong and Ármód's sons took hold of one end of the beam and Thorgils, Lambi, and Gudrún's sons the other. They heaved so hard on the beam that it broke asunder in the middle. Right at that moment Hardbein thrust his halberd out where the door had burst apart. This stab struck on Thorstein the Black's steel cap and glided off into his forehead and that was a very nasty gash. Then Thorstein said — and a truer word was never spoken — that there was somebody at home all right. Next thing they knew, Helgi bolted out past the door, so swiftly and boldly that those standing nearest gave way. Thorgils was close by at that moment and slashed at him with his sword; the blow landed on his shoulder and made a deep cut. Helgi then turned on Thorgils with a wood axe in his hand, and said: "Old as I am, I'm still not afraid to look a weapon in the eye," and he flung the axe at Thorgils and it landed on his foot and that was a bad wound. When Bolli saw this, he made a dash at Helgi with Footbite in his hand and ran him through with it. That was his death wound. Straightway Helgi's two followers dashed out of the hut and Hardbein too. Thorleik Bollason set on Eyjólf, who was a strong fellow. Thorleik laid on a blow with his sword and it landed on his thigh just above the knee and took off his leg, and he fell down to the ground dead. Húnbogi the Strong took Thorgils on and struck at him with an axe, and the blow landed on his back and cleaved him asunder at the waist. Thórd Cat was standing near there when Hardbein darted out. Thórd wanted to make a dash for him right away, but Bolli ran over there as soon as he saw this and told him not to harm Hardbein. "No one here is to commit a dastard's deed, and Hardbein is to be given quarter."

Helgi had another son by the name of Skorri. He was being fostered on the farm called England in southern Reykjardal.

65

Outwitted by Snorri

AFTER these doings Thorgils and his men rode away, crossing over
the ridge into Reykjardal where they announced the killings. Then
they rode back west the same way they had come, and did not stop
until they came to Hordadal. They now told what had happened and
what they had accomplished. This raid of theirs was the subject of
much talk, and it was thought a great deed that such a fighter as
Helgi had been brought down. Thorgils thanked the men for having
come along and Bolli's sons did the same. The men who had been
along with Thorgils then went their ways. Lambi rode west to Laxárdal and stopped first at Hjardarholt and gave his kinsmen a detailed
account of the happenings in Skorradal. They expressed their disapproval of his part in it and held it very much against him, saying
that he had shown himself to be more akin to Thorbjorn Skrjúp
than to Mýrkjartan, king of the Irish. Lambi got very angry at their
railing and said it certainly was not very decent of them to upbraid
him like that — "for it is I who have snatched you from death," he
said. After that they had little to say to one another, for each side
was more disgruntled than ever. Lambi then rode home.

Thorgils Holluson rode out to Helgafell and with him Gudrún's
sons and his foster brothers Halldór and Ornólf. They arrived at Helgafell rather late at night after all were in bed. Gudrún got up and
told everyone else to get up and wait upon the guests. She went into
the guesthall and greeted Thorgils and the others and asked for
news. Thorgils returned Gudrún's greeting. He had by then laid off
his cloak and his weapons and was sitting leaned up against the
pillar supports. He wore a reddish-brown kirtle and had a wide silver
belt around his waist. Gudrún sat down next to him on the bench.
Then Thorgils spoke this verse:

> To Helgi's home a raid we led.
> With the corpse the ravens fed,
> Stained all red oaken shield,
> Following Thorleik's tracks afield.
> Felled we there warriors three,

The very best one e'er could see,
So keen was each, a helmet's tree.[1]
Avengéd Bolli now have we.

Gudrún asked them in detail about the things that had happened
on their raid. Thorgils replied to all she asked. Gudrún said they had
taken care of their errand speedily and thoroughly and gave them her
thanks for it. After that they were served with meat and drink and
when they had had their fill, they were shown to their beds. They
slept the night through.

Next morning Thorgils went to have a talk with Gudrún and said:
"As you well know, Gudrún, I have now carried out this task which
you asked of me, and I think I can say it has been done manfully and
well. Besides, I trust I have not done all this for nothing. You no
doubt also recall what you have promised me in return for this. I now
feel that I am entitled to that part of the bargain." Then Gudrún
said: "Not so much time has passed since we spoke to one another
about this that I have forgotten it. I, for my part, have no other intention but to hold to everything we agreed upon. Just what do you
recall was our bargain?" Thorgils said she no doubt remembered that.
Gudrún replied: "I think what I promised was not to marry any man
here in the country except you. Or do you want to raise any objection
to that?" Thorgils said she recalled it correctly. "That is fine," said
Gudrún, "if we two remember one and the same thing about this
matter. I'm not going to put you off any longer, for I don't think I'm
destined to become your wife. I believe I am keeping to every word of
our agreement if I marry Thorkel Eyjólfsson, for he is not here in
the country at present." Then Thorgils turned very red and said: "I
plainly see which way the wind blows — I have always felt a cold
draught from that quarter. You don't have to tell me, these are Snorri
Godi's schemes." With that Thorgils jumped to his feet and broke off
their talk, for he was seething with rage. He went to his companions
and told them he wanted to be off. Thorleik was ill-pleased that
things had not turned out to suit Thorgils, but Bolli took his mother's
part in the matter. Gudrún said she would give Thorgils good gifts
and try to smooth it over with him that way. Thorleik said there
would be no use in that — "for Thorgils is much too proud-minded a
man to want to stoop for such trifles." Gudrún said that in that case he

would have to comfort himself at home. Thereupon Thorgils rode off from Helgafell and his foster brothers with him. He came home to Tunga and was most ill-content with his lot.

66

"Closer Neighbors"

THAT winter Ósvíf took sick and died. His death was considered a great loss, for he had been a very sage man. Ósvíf was buried at Helgafell, for Gudrún had had a church built there. That same winter Gest Oddleifsson fell sick; and when the illness came heavy upon him, he called for his son Thórd the Short and said: "I have a feeling that this sickness will mean the parting of our ways. I want to be brought to Helgafell for burial, for I have a feeling that that place will become foremost in these parts. From there I have often seen a light shining."[1] After that Gest died.

The winter had been cold and there was a layer of ice extending far out into the Breidafjord so that no ship could leave from Bardastrond. Gest's body was laid out for two nights at Hagi. On the last of these nights such a sharp wind came up that all the ice was driven away from shore, and the next day the weather was fine and calm. Thórd took a ship and laid Gest's body on board, and they sailed south that day across the Breidafjord and came in the evening to Helgafell. Thórd was made welcome and stayed there overnight. In the morning Gest's body was put into the ground; he was laid to rest in the same grave as Ósvíf. Thus what Gest foretold came true —that they would be closer neighbors than when the one lived at Bardastrond and the other in Saelingsdal.[2]

Thórd the Short went home as soon as this mission was finished. That very next night a wild storm came up and drove all the ice back in along the shore. It held for a long time that winter so that there was no passing of ships. It seemed a great wonder that they just so happened to get across with Gest's body when there was no crossing that winter before or afterwards.

67

Yet a Twist

THERE was a man called Thórarin who lived in Langadal. He had
the title of *godi* but was not a powerful man. His son's name was
Audgísl. He was an alert and quick fellow. Thorgils Holluson got
the *godi* title away from them both, and they felt this as the greatest
disgrace. Audgísl went to see Snorri Godi and told him of this in-
justice and asked for his support. Snorri had a ready answer on the
one hand but committed himself on the whole neither one way nor
the other, saying: "So this gawk of a Halla's son[1] is pushing himself
forward and putting on airs, is he? I wonder if anyone will ever
come along who will stand up against Thorgils. There's no denying
he is a big, hardy fellow, but it has happened before that his sort
has been struck dead." Snorri gave Audgísl an ornamented axe when
he went away.

In the spring Thorgils Holluson and Thorstein the Black went
south to the Borgarfjord country to make offers of amends to Helgi's
sons and other kinsmen of his. They came to an agreement on this
and honorable payment was made. Thorstein paid two thirds of the
compensation for the killing. Thorgils was to pay the other third and
make the payment at the Thing.

That summer Thorgils rode to the Thing; and just as they were
coming up to the lava field at Thingvellir, they saw a woman coming
toward them. She was unusually big. Thorgils rode to meet her, but
she turned away saying:

> Fighters beware,
> Brave though ye be,
> And wary watch for
> The wiles of Snorri;
> Wary enough ye will not be;
> Wise is Snorri.

Then she turned and went her way. Thorgils said: "It seldom
happened, when it boded well, that you went from the Thing when
I was on my way there." Thorgils now rode on to the Thing and to
his booth, and all was quiet through the first part of the meeting.

One day everybody had his clothes hanging out to dry. Thorgils had a blue hooded cloak which was spread out on the wall of the booth, and it was heard to say:

> Wet it hangs on the wall,
> Wot the cloak a trick,
> Ne'er more dry after this,
> Nor hide I, it likely wot yet a twist.

This was thought a great wonder.

The next day Thorgils went west across the river to make the payment to Helgi's sons. He sat down on the rocky flat above the booths. With him was his foster brother Halldór and many other men. Helgi's sons came over to meet them. Thorgils began counting out the silver. Audgísl Thórarinsson came by there, and just when Thorgils counted ten, Audgísl swung at him, and they all thought they heard the head call eleven as it flew off his neck. Audgísl made a dash for the booths of the Vatnsfirthers, but Halldór was right at his heels and struck him down dead in the doorway. The news that Thorgils Holluson had been killed also came to Snorri Godi's booth. Snorri said: "You probably didn't hear right; more likely Thorgils Holluson has done the killing." The man answered: "All the same his head flew off from his trunk." "Then it may well be true," said Snorri. These manslaughters were settled as is told in the saga of Thorgils Holluson.[2]

68

"Wise is Snorri"

THE SAME summer that Thorgils Holluson was killed a ship came into Bjarnarhofn. Thorkel Eyjólfsson was its owner. He was by then such a wealthy man that he had two trading vessels. The other one came into the Hrútafjord at Bordeyr; and both were loaded with timber. As soon as Snorri Godi heard of Thorkel's arrival, he rode straightway to the ship. Thorkel gave him a very friendly welcome. He also had a good supply of drink on board and it was given out liberally; there was much talk between them. Snorri asked for news from Norway, and Thorkel gave good account of everything in detail. Snorri in turn told what had happened in Iceland while Thorkel had been abroad. "The best thing now, it would seem to me," said Snorri, "would be for you to do as I suggested before you went away — give up the trading business, settle down and get yourself a wife, and none other than the very one we talked about before." Thorkel answered: "I know what you're driving at. I too am of the same mind now as when we talked it over, for I don't begrudge myself such a fine marriage if it can be brought about." Snorri said: "I am quite ready and willing to plead this suit on your behalf. And now both things are taken care of which you felt stood most in the way of your getting Gudrún — Bolli is avenged and Thorgils has been done away with." Thorkel said: "Your counsels, Snorri, do indeed run deep, and I most certainly want to bend all effort toward this suit."

Snorri stayed at the ship some nights. Then they took a ten-oared boat which was afloat there beside the merchant vessel and set out, twenty-five of them. They went to Helgafell. Gudrún made Snorri most welcome, and they were served with the best in the house. After they had been there one night, Snorri asked Gudrún for a talk and said: "This is the way the situation stands: I have made this trip on behalf of my friend Thorkel Eyjólfsson, who has come here, as you can see, for no other reason than to sue for your hand. He is a man of good standing, and as for his family and reputation, you already know about that. He doesn't lack for money either. I think he is now the one man here in the west who shows the greatest promise of becoming a chieftain, if he but chooses to. Thorkel has always been highly respected whenever he has been out here in Iceland, and is counted even more highly when he is in Norway with noble men." Gudrún then replied: "My sons Thorleik and Bolli will have the most to say in this. But you Snorri, are the third person to whom I shall entrust those decisions which matter most to me, for you have long been a sound and faithful adviser." Snorri said he took it to be self-evident that Thorkel should not be turned down.

After that Snorri had Gudrún's sons called and took the matter up with them and set forth what a great asset Thorkel could be to them with all his money and wise judgment, and he put his words very smoothly. Then Bolli answered: "My mother no doubt is best judge of this, and I am willing to go along with whatever she wishes. And we of course take well into account that it is you, Snorri, who are pleading this case, for you have done us a good turn many a time." Then Gudrún said: "We shall have to rely very much on Snorri's judgment in this. For your advice to us, Snorri, has always been sound." Snorri used all his power of persuasion, and the upshot of it all was that a marriage was arranged between Gudrún and Thorkel. Snorri offered to have the feast at his farmstead. Thorkel was very pleased with this — "for I don't lack for supplies and can furnish you with whatever you like." Then Gudrún said: "It is my wish that this wedding feast be here at Helgafell. I won't blench at having to stand the cost. I don't want Thorkel or anybody else to have the burden of it." "You often show, Gudrún," said Snorri, "that you are a most exceptional woman."

So it was arranged that the wedding should be at Helgafell six weeks before the end of summer. Thereupon Snorri and Thorkel left, the one for home, the other for his ship. During the summer he spent his time, by turns, either at Tunga or at his ship. The time was at hand for the wedding feast, and Gudrún was busy making preparations and laying in supplies. Snorri Godi came to the feast with Thorkel; they had nearly sixty in their company and it was a very select one, for most of the people were in brightly colored array. Gudrún had nearly a hundred guests there waiting to welcome them. The brothers Bolli and Thorleik and all Gudrún's guests went out to meet Snorri and his party. They were given a very fine welcome; their horses and clothes were taken care of, and they were shown into the guest hall. Thorkel and Snorri and their party occupied the high bench of honor, and Gudrún's guests the lower bench.[1]

69

Gudrún's Highhandedness

THAT autumn GunnarThidrandabani (Thidrandi's Slayer) had been
sent to Gudrún for sheltering and help, and she had taken him in
and his name had been kept secret. Gunnar had been put under
outlawry for the killing of Thidrandi Geitisson from Krossavík, as is
told in the saga of the Njardvikings.[1] He stayed in close hiding, for
there were many powerful men who were keeping a lookout for
him.

The first evening of the feast, when the people were going to the
water to wash, a big man was standing there by the water. He was
broad-shouldered and broad-chested and had a hat on his head.
Thorkel asked who he was. He gave some name or other that occurred to him. Thorkel said: "You are hardly telling the truth. You
fit more the description of Gunnar Thidrandabani. And if you are
such a great and fearless fighter as people say, you won't want to
keep your name secret." Then Gunnar answered: "You seem extremely eager to find out, and I don't see any reason for hiding it
from you. You have correctly recognized your man. So now what do
you propose to do with me?" Thorkel said he would find that out
soon enough and told his men to seize him.

Gudrún was sitting inside on the cross dais with other women
about her, their heads coifed in white linen. As soon as she became
aware of what was going on, she got down from the bridal bench
and called to her men to lend Gunnar a hand, ordering them to spare
no man of them who might want to start trouble. Gudrún had a
much larger force than Thorkel, so it looked as though things
would take a different turn from what had been expected.

Snorri Godi stepped between the men and told them to calm the
storm — "and as for you, Thorkel, you have no other recourse but
to leave off pressing the point. You can see for yourself what a remarkable woman Gudrún is when she can get the best of both of
us." Thorkel explained that he had promised his namesake, Thorkel
Geitisson, that he would kill Gunnar, should he ever get to the

west districts — "and Thorkel is a very good friend of mine." Snorri
said: "You are much more under obligation to do our bidding; and
for you personally this is of prime importance, for no matter how far
you search, you'll never again find such a wife as Gudrún." When
Snorri put it that way to Thorkel — who could see for himself that
what Snorri said was true — he calmed down and Gunnar was safely
led off for that evening.

The feast got on well after that, and was a splendid one. When it
was over, everyone made ready to leave, and Thorkel gave presents
of great value to Snorri and to all the other prominent guests. Snorri
invited Bolli Bollason home with him and told him he could stay
with him anytime or all the time, just as he thought best. Bolli accepted and rode home with him to Tunga.

Thorkel settled down now at Helgafell and took charge of the
farm. It could soon be seen that he was no worse a hand at that than
at trading enterprises. That very fall he had the sleeping hall torn
down, and by winter another was back up, and it was a large and
stately building. Thorkel and Gudrún grew to love one another
deeply.

The winter drew to a close, and in the spring Gudrún asked Thorkel what he intended to do about Gunnar Thidrandabani. Thorkel
said it was up to her to decide — "You have taken so strong a hand
in this matter that probably nothing else will do, short of his being
sent off honorably." Gudrún said he had guessed right. "I want you
to give him a ship," she said, "and along with that everything he has
need of." Thorkel answered and smiled: "You are not small-minded
on many a score, Gudrún," he said," it would never do for you tc
have a skinflint for a husband — that would hardly suit your nature.
It shall be done as you wish." And carried out it was. Gunnar accepted the gift gratefully. "I shall never be so 'long-armed' as to be
able to pay you back for all the favors you have shown me," he said.
Gunnar sailed abroad and made Norway. After that he returned to
his own estates. Gunnar was very wealthy, a truly great man, and a
fine fellow.

70

Thorleik and Bolli

THORKEL Eyjólfsson became a great chieftain and went to much trouble to acquire friends and esteem. He was an influential man in his district and a great prosecutor of the law. His dealings at the Thing are not mentioned here however. Next to Snorri, Thorkel was the most powerful man in Breidafjord during his lifetime. He kept his farm in good shape and had all the houses at Helgafell enlarged and made comfortable. He also laid the groundwork for a church and let it be known that he intended to go abroad and get himself some church timber. Gudrún and Thorkel had a son who was called Gellir; he early grew up to be a most promising lad.

Bolli Bollason was living in turns either at Tunga or at Helgafell. Snorri was very kind to him. Bolli's brother Thorleik stayed at Helgafell. These brothers were big men, and very stalwart, but Bolli was the foremost in all things. Thorkel was kind to his stepchildren. Gudrún loved Bolli the best of all her children; he was now sixteen years old, and Thorleik twenty. One day Thorleik told his stepfather and his mother that he wanted to go abroad. "I'm tired of sitting at home like the womenfolk and would like the means and wares to be got for me for the voyage," he said. Thorkel answered: "I don't think I have ever thwarted you brothers as long as we have been related. It seems to me most understandable that you are eager to learn about life and the ways of others. For I imagine you'll be thought a valiant fellow among capable men wherever you go." Thorleik said he did not want to have many wares along — "for it is uncertain how well I can manage, young and inexperienced in many things as I am." Thorkel said he could have as much as he wanted.

After that Thorkel bought Thorleik interest in a ship which was drawn up at Dogurdarnes. Thorkel saw him off to the ship and had him well fitted out in everything for the voyage. In the summer Thorleik sailed away, and the ship made Norway. The ruler of the country at that time was King Óláf, the Saint. Thorleik went straightway to see King Óláf, who received him cordially and recognized him from his line of kin and invited him to stay with him. Thorleik gratefully accepted. He stayed with the king over the winter and became one of the guard, and the king esteemed him highly. Thorleik was thought a most valiant fellow, and stayed on with King Óláf several years.

But now to tell of Bolli Bollason. The spring when he was eighteen years old, he talked with his stepfather Thorkel and his mother and said he wanted them to pay out his share of his father's inheritance. Gudrún asked what he was intending to do since he demanded this payment from them. Bolli answered: "It is my wish that a woman be wooed on my behalf, and I would like you, Thorkel, to be my spokesman in this suit and see that it goes through." Thorkel asked what woman he had in mind. Bolli answered: "The woman's name is Thórdís; she is the daughter of Snorri Godi, and is the one I would most like to have; and should I not get her, I'll be in no hurry to marry. So it means a great deal to me that this be carried through." Thorkel replied: "It is no more than fair to you, stepson, that I plead this suit on your behalf, if it makes such a great difference to you. I daresay this suit can be easily won with Snorri, for he will be able to see that he is being made a good offer where you are concerned." Gudrún said: "I might quickly add, Thorkel, that I'll leave nothing undone so that Bolli gets the one marriage match he wants; and that is for two reasons — I love him best and he has always been that one of my children who could be relied upon to do my will." Thorkel asserted that he for his part had every intention of doing well by Bolli in starting him out — "for that is only meet on many accounts; and I daresay, anyone would be getting a good catch in Bolli."

Not long after that Thorkel and Bolli set out, and many others along with them. They kept going until they came to Tunga. Snorri gave them a fine and friendly welcome, and did all he could to be most cordial. Thórdís Snorradóttir was living at home with her father. She was fair to behold and a remarkable woman. After they had spent a few days at Tunga, Thorkel brought up the subject of the proposal and suggested a marriage tie between their two families, asking Snorri for his daughter Thórdís' hand on behalf of Bolli. Snorri answered: "Such a proposal is well tendered, as I would expect of you; and I want to give you a favorable answer to this suit, for I think Bolli is a most promising young man and any woman married to him is well married. But all the same it will depend mostly on how Thórdís feels about it, for she is to have only that husband who is after her own heart."

So the proposal was broached to Thórdís and her answer was that she would rely on her father's judgment in this and she said that she would rather marry Bolli from her own district than some unknown man from farther away. As soon as Snorri saw that she had nothing against being married to Bolli, everything was settled and the betrothal took place. Snorri was to have the wedding feast at his farm and that was to be in midsummer. With this Thorkel and Bolli rode back home to Helgafell, and Bolli stayed home until time for the wedding. Then Thorkel and Bolli got ready to leave and with them all those who were expected to come along. Together they were a large and most imposing company. They set out on their way and came to Tunga, where they got a very fine welcome. There was a large gathering present and the feast was a splendid one. When it drew to a close, everyone made ready to leave. Snorri gave honorable gifts to Thorkel and Gudrún, and likewise to his other friends and relatives. Now all who had been guests at the feast rode back to their own homes. Bolli stayed on at Tunga, and he and Thórdís soon grew to love one another dearly. Snorri went to great pains to do well by Bolli and was even much better to him than to his own children. Bolli accepted all this gratefully and stayed at Tunga throughout that year and stood in high favor.

In the summer a ship from abroad came into the Hvítá. Thorleik Bollason had half interest in it, and some Norwegians owned the other half. When Bolli learned of the arrival of his brother, he straightway rode south to Borgarfjord and to the ship. The brothers were glad to see one another. Bolli stayed there for several days, then the two of them rode west to Helgafell. Thorkel and Gudrún both gave them a hearty welcome and asked Thorleik to stay on there over the winter, an offer he gratefully accepted. Thorleik remained at Helgafell for a while and then he rode to the Hvítá and had his ship put up and his goods moved west. Thorleik had fared well, gaining both fame and fortune, for he had become a retainer to that noblest of all men, King Óláf, the Saint. He stayed now at Helgafell throughout the winter, and Bolli at Tunga.

71

Appeasement Won

THAT winter the brothers Thorleik and Bolli were always getting together and conversing off by themselves and never took any pleasure in games or other amusement. And one time when Thorleik was at Tunga, the brothers kept on with their discussion all day and all night. Snorri then suspected that they might be plotting something big. So he went over to join them in their talk. They greeted him well, but abruptly let their conversation drop. Snorri duly returned their greeting. Then he said: "What plans do you two have in the making that you pay no attention to eating or to sleeping?" Bolli answered: "There aren't any plots or plans; what we have to talk about is of little account." When Snorri saw that they wanted to hide from him whatever it was they had on their minds, he suspected all the more that they might be talking about something which would lead to great trouble if carried out. So he said to them: "I have my doubts that you two have been making idle jokes or gossiping all this time. Not that I would blame you if that were so, but please tell me and don't try to hide it from me. All of us together can't possibly make a decision for the worse, for no matter what it is I will not stand in the way of its being carried out if you gain in honor by it." Thorleik thought Snorri had their interest at heart and so he told him in a few words that their plan was to attack Óláf's sons and make them pay dearly, adding that they no longer fell short of being on equal footing with them, now that Thorleik was one of King Óláf's guard and Bolli had married into the family of such a chieftain as Snorri. Snorri had this to say: "Enough was done to offset Bolli's killing when Helgi Hardbeinsson paid for it with his life. People have had more than enough of these troubles already, even if an end should be made of them at last." Then Bolli said: "What's this now, Snorri, aren't you just as keen on backing us up as you let on a little while ago? Indeed, Thorleik would never have told you of this plan, had he asked my advice first. And as for your making out that Helgi's life settled the score for Bolli's, people happen to know that wergild paid off Helgi's killing and my father still remains unavenged."

When Snorri saw that he could not get them to change their minds, he said he was prepared to try for a peaceful settlement with Óláf's sons rather than have manslaughter begin all over again. This the brothers agreed to. Then Snorri rode off to Hjardarholt with some men.

Halldór made him welcome and invited him to stay there. Snorri said he must ride back home that night — "but I have an urgent matter to take up with you." Then they began talking and Snorri made his errand known, saying that he had learned that Bolli and Thorleik were no longer content to let them get off without paying for Bolli's killing — "so now I would like to try for a peaceful settlement and see if there can't be an end to this hapless state of affairs between you kinsmen." Halldór did not take this amiss and answered: "I know only too well that Thorgils Holluson and Bolli's sons had it in mind to go after me and my brothers before you turned their vengeance in another direction and made them feel it was best to kill Helgi Hardbeinsson instead. You have been very good and decent about this matter, whatever your share may have been in former dealings with us kinsmen." Snorri replied: "It means a great deal to me that my efforts aren't wasted and that what I have my heart most set on can be achieved, namely a lasting peace between you kinsmen. For I well know the character and temperament of those who have these charges against you and am sure that they will faithfully abide by whatever they agree to." Halldór answered: "If that is also the will of my brothers, I will consent to paying out money for Bolli's killing, as much as those elected to arbitrate decide on. But I want to make an exemption of all outlawry and my *godi* title, as well as my farm and property. I also want to exempt those farms and properties on which my brothers live, and stipulate that they have free possession of them before this agreement is closed. Moreover each side may pick his man for the arbitration." Snorri said: "This is indeed a splendid offer and Thorleik and Bolli will accept it if they are at all willing to take my advice."

Then Snorri rode back home and told the brothers the outcome of his errand and also that he would have nothing whatsoever to do with their case if they did not accept these terms. Bolli bade him make the decision — "and I want you, Snorri, to be the arbitrator on our behalf." Then Snorri sent word to Halldór, saying that the terms were agreed to and asking him to choose a man to stand up against him for arbitration. Halldór chose Steinthór Thorláksson from Eyr. The meeting for the settlement was to be at Drangar on Skógarstrond when four weeks of summer had passed. Thorleik Bollason rode back to Helgafell, and nothing to speak of happened during that winter.

When the time set for the meeting was at hand, Snorri Godi came with Bolli's sons in a party of fifteen. Steinthór came to the meeting with equally as many. Snorri and Steinthór took up their talk and came to an agreement about the case and set the fines, but it is not told how much they came to. All that is said is that the money was paid out rightly and the terms were faithfully kept. It was at the Thórsnes Thing that the payments were made. Halldór gave Bolli a fine sword, and Steinthór Óláfsson gave Thorleik a shield, and that was also a very fine gift. Thereafter the Thing came to an end, and both sides felt they had gained in honor from these dealings.

72

Brothers in Partnership

AFTER Bolli and Thorleik and the sons of Óláf became reconciled and Thorleik had spent one winter in Iceland, Bolli let it be known that he intended to go abroad. Snorri discouraged this, saying: "It seems to me there is much at stake in how it will turn out for you. But if you are desirous of having more in your possession and power than you now have, I am willing to get land and property and build a homestead for you, and along with that see to it that you get a chieftainship, and I shall do all I can to further your esteem. I daresay that will come easy, for most people bear you good will." Bolli replied: "I have had it in mind for a long time to go to the countries to the south just once. A person certainly doesn't know much if he hasn't seen anything outside of Iceland." And when Snorri saw that Bolli was firmly set on this and that nothing would avail to dissuade him, Snorri made him an offer of as much money and goods as he wanted for his journey. Bolli accepted this and said he wanted to have a good deal of money along. "I don't want to have to accept anyone's charity, either here or abroad," he said.

Afterwards Bolli rode south to Borgarfjord and to the Hvítá and bought the other half share in Thorleik's ship from the men that owned it. Now the brothers owned the ship together. Then Bolli rode back west and home.

Bolli and Thórdís had a daughter. She was called Herdís and Gudrún offered to foster her. She was one year old when she went to Helgafell. Thórdís also stayed there for a long time, and Gudrún was very good to her too.

73

Thorleik and Bolli with King Óláf Haraldsson

Now BOTH of the brothers went to the ship. Bolli had many wares along. They fitted out the ship, and when they were all ready, they put out to sea. They did not get a fair wind and were out at sea a long time, making Norway in the fall north at Trondheim. King Óláf who had his seat in Vík, was there in the east of the country at the time and had made arrangements to stay there over the winter. When the brothers learned that the king would not be coming north to Trondheim that fall, Thorleik said he wanted to sail on east to see King Óláf, following the coast all the way. Bolli answered: "I don't think much of drifting about from one merchant town to another in the fall of the year. That seems like a lot of hardship and privation to me. I want to stay right here in town over the winter. I've been told that the king will come north in the spring. If he doesn't come, I won't stand in the way of our going to him." Bolli had his way. So they unloaded their ship and got themselves quarters in town.

It soon became evident that Bolli was eager to push himself forward and wanted to outdo others; and in that he succeeded, for he was an openhanded fellow. He soon gained much esteem in Norway. Bolli had a lot of followers that winter in Trondheim, and whenever he went to drinking bouts, one could easily see that his men were better dressed and equipped with weapons than the other townsmen. Moreover, he paid for all his comrades too, whenever they sat at their drinking. This went hand in hand with his liberalness and generosity in other things. So the brothers stayed in town throughout the winter.

King Óláf held his seat in Sarpsborg[1] that winter, and it was rumored from the east that the king was not expected to come north. Early in the spring the brothers got their ship ready and sailed east down along the coast. They had a smooth voyage and arrived at Sarpsborg and went straightway to see King Óláf. He welcomed his retainer Thorleik together with his comrades. Then the king asked who the man of such stately bearing was, whom Thorleik had in his company. Thorleik answered: "That is my brother and his name is Bolli." "He certainly is an exceptional fellow," said the king. After that the king invited the brothers to stay with him. They accepted gratefully and were with the king that spring. The king treated Thorleik just as well as before, but all the same he esteemed Bolli much more, for in his opinion Bolli was a paragon among men.

Toward the end of spring, the brothers talked over their plans for traveling. Thorleik asked Bolli whether he intended going out to Iceland in the summer — "or do you want to stay in Norway longer?" Bolli answered: "I am going to do neither. To tell you the truth, when I left Iceland I hadn't planned that people get news of me from just next door. I would like you, kinsman, to take over our ship now." Thorleik thought it a shame for them to have to part — "but you, Bolli, will have your way in this as in other things." They brought the matter before the king and he answered: "Don't you want to stay with us longer, Bolli? I would think it best if you would stay with me for a time. I will give you the same rank as I have given your brother." Bolli replied: "I would be more than happy, my lord, to be in your service, but first I want to travel on abroad as I had previously planned and visit those places I have so much longed to see.

But I will gladly accept the choice you offer if I am destined to return." "You are the one to decide about your travelings," said the king, "for you Icelanders are a stubborn lot in most things. All the same I want to say as final words that you, Bolli, are in my opinion the most noteworthy man who has come from Iceland in my day."

So when Bolli had permission from the king, he made ready to leave and went aboard a merchant vessel that was bound for Denmark. He had many wares with him, and some of his companions went along too. He and King Óláf took leave of one another in great friendship, and the king gave Bolli valuable gifts at parting. Thorleik stayed on with King Óláf, and Bolli continued his travelings, finally coming south to Denmark. There he stayed during the winter and received great honor from men of high rank. Nor was he any the less magnificent and gallant in Denmark than he had been when he was in Norway. After Bolli had been in Denmark one winter, he set out again for foreign parts and did not let up with his travels until he came all the way to Miklagard.[2] He had been there only a short while when he became one of the Varangian guard.[3] As far as we know, no Norseman had ever entered the service of the king of Miklagard before Bolli Bollason. He stayed in Miklagard a good many years and was thought to be a most stalwart fellow in every test of manhood and was always right up with the foremost. The Varangians esteemed Bolli highly the whole time he was in Miklagard.

74

Thorkel's Conceit

Now WE must take up the story where we left Thorkel Eyjólfsson sitting on his farmstead in high estate, enjoying his chieftainship. His and Gudrún's son Gellir grew up there at home and was soon a manly fellow and popular. One time Thorkel told Gudrún a dream he had had: "I had a dream," he said, "and it seemed to me that I had a beard so big it spread out over all Breidafjord." Thorkel asked her to interpret the dream. Gudrún asked him: "What do you think this dream means?" "It seems clear to me that my power will extend over the whole of Breidafjord." "Maybe so," replied Gudrún, "but it rather looks to me that your beard will be taking a dip[1] into the Breidafjord."

That same summer Thorkel launched his ship and made ready to go to Norway. His son Gellir was then twelve years old and went abroad with his father. Thorkel had announced that he was going for the purpose of procuring timber for his church. When all was in readiness, he put out to sea and had an easy voyage, but not a particularly short one. They made Norway to the north. King Óláf was then holding his seat in Trondheim. Thorkel and his son Gellir went directly to see King Óláf. They were well received there. Thorkel was thought of so highly by the king that winter that it was common talk the king had given him no less than one hundred marks of pure uncoined silver. At Yule the king gave Gellir a cloak, and that too was a choice and expensive gift.

That winter King Óláf was having a church built in town out of timber. It was designed to be a minster of large size and everything for it was carefully selected. In the spring the timber which the king had given Thorkel was loaded onto his ship; and large and fine timber it was too — Thorkel had seen to that. It happened one morning early when the king was walking about with a few followers that he saw a man up on top of the church being built there in town. He was most astonished for it was a good deal earlier in the morning than the workmen were used to being up. The king recognized the man. There was Thorkel Eyjólfsson and he was putting the measuring rod to all the largest beams: the crossbeams, the sills, and the upright supports. The king headed right over there and said: "What's this now, Thorkel, are you thinking of fashioning the timber you are freighting to Iceland after this church here?" Thorkel replied: "That's the truth of it, my lord." Then King Óláf spoke: "Now you just cut off two ells from every beam, and that church of yours will still be the biggest one ever built in Iceland." Thorkel answered: "You can keep your wood, if you think you have given away too much or have regrets on second thought, but not one ell will I cut off. I've enough initiative and drive to get myself some other wood." Then the king said to him, gently and soberly: "Two things can certainly be said of you, Thorkel — you are a man of much account, but now you are putting on too big airs for your own good. For it is nothing but presumption for a peasant's son to think of vying with us. It is not true, however, that I begrudge you the timber if you are destined to build a church out of it, for your church could never be big enough to hold all your conceit. But it is near my guess that people will have little good of this timber and you will be far from getting anything made out of it."

After that they broke off talking and the king turned away; it was easy to see that he thought it for the worse that Thorkel had no intention of heeding at all what he said. But all the same the king did not let it be known openly, and he and Thorkel parted in kindly affection.

Thorkel boarded his ship and put out to sea. They got a good wind and their crossing was not long. Thorkel sailed his ship into the Hrútafjord, and rode straightway from his ship home to Helgafell. Everyone was happy to see him. Thorkel had got much honor on this journey. He had his ship put up and enclosed and the church timber stored away where it was safe, for he did not have a chance to move it down from the north that fall, as he was always too busy.

Thorkel now sat at home on his farm throughout the winter. He had a Yule drinking at Helgafell and it was very well attended, and all in all he carried on in great estate that winter. And Gudrún put no stop to it, but said that was what money was for — to increase your pride and prestige; and whatever Gudrún needed in order to live in grand style had to be on hand. That winter Thorkel shared with his friends many of the treasures he had brought from abroad.

CHART 23

THORKEL EYJÓLFSSON'S RELATION TO THORSTEIN KUGGASON

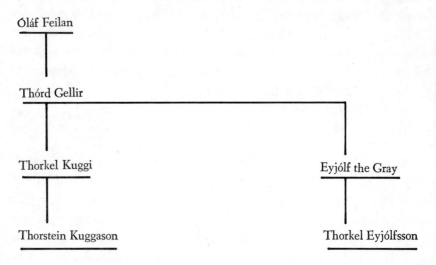

75

Bargaining Awry

THAT winter after Yule Thorkel prepared to go north to Hrútafjord to move his timber down south. First he rode into the Dales and then into Ljárskógar to his kinsman Thorstein, where he got men and horses. He then went north to Hrútafjord and stayed there some time making arrangements for the transport, and rounding up horses for himself there about the fjord, for he did not want to make several trips if he could help it. All this was not done quickly, and Thorkel was busy at the job far into Lent. He got the work finally underway however, and it took more than twenty horses to bring the wood south, where it was left lying at Ljáreyr. Later he intended to move it by ship over to Helgafell. Thorstein had a big ferry boat, and Thorkel planned on using it when he started for home. Thorkel stayed at Ljárskógar during Lent, for these two kinsmen were very fond of one another.

One day Thorstein said to Thorkel that it would be a convenient

time to ride over to Hjardarholt. "I want to make Halldór a bid for
his land, for he hasn't had much livestock ever since he paid Bolli's
sons the indemnity for their father. And that land is just what I
would most like to own." Thorkel said it was up to him. So they rode
from home, a good twenty of them together. They came to Hjardarholt, and Halldór received them well and was very talkative. There
were but few men at home, since Halldór had sent some men up
north to Steingrímsfjord; a whale had come ashore there which he
had a share in. Beinir the Strong was at home; he was the only one
still alive of those who had been in Óláf Peacock's household. Halldór had spoken to Beinir as soon as he had seen Thorstein and his
men riding up — "I know full well just what business these kinsmen
are on. They will want to make me an offer for my land. And if that
is so, they will call me aside for a talk. It is my guess that they will sit
down, one on either side of me, and if they show signs of giving me
any trouble, then you aren't to be any slower in setting on Thorstein
than I on Thorkel; you have long been faithful to us kinsmen. I have
also sent to the neighboring farms for some men. I am hoping that
the two things take place at about the same time, that the help comes
when we are just about finishing our talk."

And as the day wore on, Thorstein suggested to Halldór that the
three of them together should have a talk — "we two have a matter
to take up with you." Halldór said that was fine with him. Thorstein
told his followers that they need not come with them, but Beinir
went along nonetheless, for things seemed to be going very much as
Halldór had guessed. They walked some distance out into the home
field. Halldór had on a cloak that was held together by a long clasp, as
was the custom then. Halldór sat down on the field, and on either
side of him each of the kinsmen, so close that they well-nigh sat
down on his cloak. But Beinir was standing over them and he had a
big axe in his hand. Then Thorstein spoke up: "My business in
coming here is that I want to buy land from you. I'm bringing this up
at this time because my kinsman Thorkel is on hand. I would think
this would be a good arrangement for us both, for I've been told that
you don't have enough livestock to run on your valuable land. I will
give you property in exchange which would be reasonable and fair,
and into the bargain whatever we can come to an agreement on."

Halldór did not take this too adversely at first, and they went on to discuss the terms of the bargain. When they thought he was near to accepting, Thorkel eagerly pushed the bargaining, wanting to bring the sale to a close. Then Halldór started stalling them off, and they tried to push the matter all the harder, and finally it came to this — the harder they pressed him, the farther he was from accepting. Then Thorkel said: "You see, kinsman Thorstein, don't you, where this is leading? He has been stalling us off the whole day with his talk, and we have been sitting here while he has made a laughing-stock of us. Now if you are really bent on buying the land, then we will have to press him even harder." At that Thorstein said he wanted to know where he stood, and told Halldór to come out into the open now and say whether he intended to sell him the land or not. Halldór answered: "I don't think there's any point in keeping you in the dark about this any longer — you will be going home tonight without a sale." Then Thorstein said: "I don't think there's any point in our putting off revealing what we already have in mind: we have thought out two choices for you, as we have reason to believe that the advantage is ours, seeing that you are outnumbered. One is that you go along with us on your own accord and have our good will in return. But the other, clearly the worse one, is that you be pressed into giving me your hand on the sale of Hjardarholt's land."

At these plain words, Halldór jumped to his feet and with such sudden force that the clasp tore out of his cloak, and he said: "Something else will have to happen first before I agree to what I don't want to do." "What will that be?" asked Thorstein. "A woodman's axe will lodge in your head, driven by some paltry fellow, and will thus put a stop to your insolence and unfairness." Thorkel answered: "That is ill-prophesied and we trust that it won't be fulfilled. But now I say there's plenty of reason, Halldór, why you should be made to forfeit your land and get nothing for it."[1] Then Halldór answered: "Sooner will you be clutching at the tangleweeds in the Breidafjord than I will ever be pressed into handing over my land for sale."

After that Halldór went home, and now the men he had sent for started drifting over to the farm. Thorstein was worked up into a rage and wanted to make an attack on Halldór at once. Thorkel told him to do nothing of the kind — "that would be a most wicked thing to do in these holy days.² But as soon as this season is past, I won't stand in the way of our having an encounter." Halldór said he would see to it that they never caught him napping. Thereupon they rode away and had much to say between themselves about this affair of theirs. Thorstein, in speaking of it, said there was no doubt about it, their errand could not have turned out worse — "but why were you, kinsman Thorkel, so afraid of setting on Halldór and putting him to shame?" Thorkel answered: "Didn't you see Beinir standing over you with raised axe? There was no way out, for he would have plunged the axe right into your head if I had made the slightest move." They rode on home to Ljárskógar. Lent was drawing to a close with only one week left.

76

Thorkel's Undoing

ON MAUNDY Thursday, early in the morning, Thorkel made ready to leave. Thorstein tried his best to dissuade him — "for the weather doesn't look dependable to me," he said. Thorkel said the weather was going to hold just fine — "and don't you try to dissuade me, kinsman, for I want to get home before Easter." So now Thorkel launched the ferry and started loading it. Thorstein carried off the timber just as fast as Thorkel and his comrades loaded it. Then Thorkel said: "Leave off with that now, kinsman, and don't try to hinder our setting out, for this is one time you'll not get your way." Thorstein answered: "That one of us who is getting his way now will be the worse off for it, and something grave is sure to happen on this trip." Thorkel assured him they would meet again hale and hearty. So Thorstein went home and was very downcast. He went into the house and asked to have a pillow laid under his head and it was done. The housemaid saw that tears rolled from his eyes down onto the pillow. A little while later the wind began to roar against the house. Then Thorstein said: "There we can hear the roar of kinsman Thorkel's doom."

But now to tell of Thorkel's trip and that of his comrades. They

sailed that day out along the Breidafjord and all told there were
twelve of them on board.[1] The wind began to blow up sharply and
rose to a full gale before it let up. They pushed on with might and
main, and these were the sturdiest of men. Thorkel had the sword
Skofnung with him and it was stuck in a beam. Thorkel and his men
sailed on until they came to Bjarnarey. People on both shores could
see him coming; and when they got there by the island, a sharp gust
smote the sail and overturned the ship. Thorkel and all the men who
were with him drowned. The church timber drifted far and wide
about the islands — the cornerstaves drifted ashore at that island
which has been called Stafey (Stave Isle) ever since. Skofnung was
stuck fast to the ribbing of the ferry and was found at Skofnungsey
(Skofnung's Isle).

The evening of the same day on which Thorkel and his men
drowned, it happened at Helgafell that Gudrún was going to the
church at just about the time when people were going to bed. And
as she passed through the gate, she saw a ghost standing before her.
It bowed down over her and spoke: "Grave tidings, Gudrún!" it
said. Gudrún answered: "Be silent about them then, wretch!"
Gudrún went on up to the church just as she had meant to, and
when she got to the door, she thought she saw Thorkel and his men
who had come home and were standing out in front of the church.
She saw that sea water was running out of their clothes. Gudrún
did not speak with them but went on into the church and stayed
there as long as seemed good to her. After that she went back to the
house, for she thought that Thorkel and his comrades might have
gone there. But when she got into the house, nobody was there. Then
Gudrún grew thoughtful over these happenings coming as they did
all at once.

On Good Friday Gudrún sent men out to get news of Thorkel's
journey, some to go in along the beaches and others out around the
islands. Wreckage had then drifted far and wide about the islands
and had washed ashore on both sides of the fjord. The Saturday
before Easter, people heard the news and thought it most grave, for
Thorkel had been a great chieftain. Thorkel was forty-eight years
old when he drowned and that was four years before King Óláf the
Saint fell.[2] Gudrún took Thorkel's loss much to heart, but bore up

under it very bravely all the same. Very little of the church timber was ever salvaged.

Gellir was then fourteen years old. He assumed the management of their farm together with his mother, and took up the chieftainship where his father had left off. He soon proved to be well suited as a leader.

Gudrún became a woman of great piety. She was the first woman in Iceland to learn the Psalter. She spent long hours at night in the church at her prayers. Herdís Bolladóttir always went with her at night, for Gudrún loved Herdís very much. It is told how one night young Herdís had a dream in which a woman came to her. She had on a woven cloak and had her head wrapped in a shawl. To Herdís the woman seemed to have the look of someone who had seen something unpleasant. She started to speak: "Tell your grandmother I'm ill-pleased with her, for she writhes on top of me night after night and lets such hot drops fall on me that I'm almost burned to a crisp. I'm telling this to you because I like you a bit better than Gudrún, and yet there's something uncanny about you too. But still I would get along with you all right if I didn't feel there was so much amiss as far as Gudrún is concerned." Then Herdís woke up and told Gudrún the dream. It seemed to Gudrún a good omen. The next morning Gudrún had the planks taken up from the church floor at the spot where she was in the habit of kneeling. Then she had the ground underneath dug up, and there they found some bones, which were black and hideous looking, also a broach and a great witch's wand. People then realized that some witch's barrow had probably been there. The bones were carried far away to a place where people were least likely to cross.

77

Bolli Bollason's Pomp

FOUR years after the drowning of Thorkel Eyjólfsson, a ship came into the Eyjafjord. That ship was owned by Bolli Bollason. Most of the oarsmen were Norwegians. Bolli had brought back many wares and precious things which great chieftains had given him. Bolli was such a man for show when he came back to Iceland from his journey that he only wanted to wear clothes of scarlet and silk, and all his weapons had gold inlay. He was called Bolli the Magnificent. He told his crew that he was going out west to his own district and left his ship and goods in charge of his men.

Bolli rode away from the ship in a party of twelve. They were all dressed in scarlet clothes, these followers of Bolli's, and rode in gilded saddles, every one a man of gallant bearing, but Bolli surpassed them all. He was in silk clothes which the king of Miklagard had given him. Outermost he had on a scarlet red cloak, and was girded with Footbite, its hilt now inlaid with gold and its haft wound in gold.[1] He had a gilded helmet on and a red shield at his side, on which a knight was traced in gold. He had a lance in his hand, as is the custom abroad in foreign lands. Wherever they took lodging, the women could not help gazing at Bolli and his companions with all their finery.

Such was the courtly style in which Bolli rode on through the west districts, arriving finally at Helgafell with his train of followers. Gudrún was overjoyed at the coming of her son Bolli. Bolli was not there long before he rode into Tunga in Saelingsdal and went to see his father-in-law Snorri and his wife Thórdís. That was a very happy meeting. Snorri invited Bolli to stay with as many of his men as he liked. Bolli accepted and stayed with Snorri all winter, he and all those men who had ridden down with him from the north. Bolli's journey brought him much fame. Snorri took no less pains now in treating Bolli with the same kindness as before when he was living with him.

78

Gudrún's Last Days

AFTER Bolli had been in Iceland one winter, Snorri Godi took sick. His illness had not come hard and suddenly upon him, so he lay bedridden for a long time. But when the sickness grew worse, he called for his kinsmen and nearest relatives. Then he spoke to Bolli:

CHART 24
Gudrún's Descendants

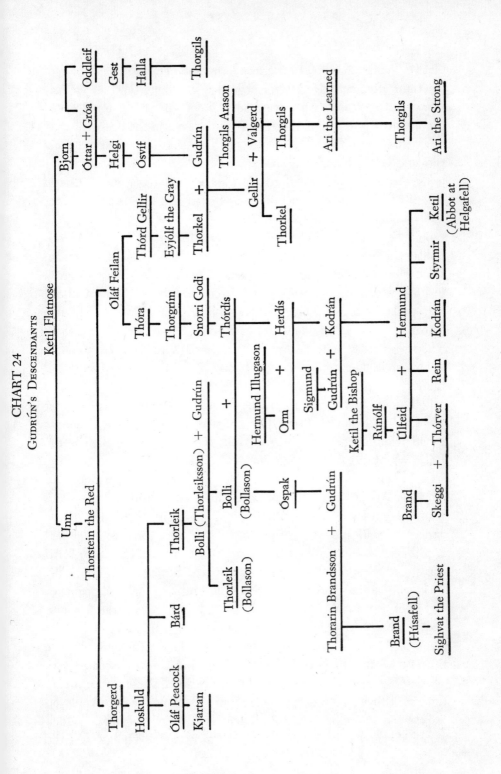

"It is my will that you take over the farmstead here and the position of chieftain after my day. I don't begrudge you honor and esteem any more than I do my own sons. And Halldór, the son of mine who I think would prove himself foremost, is not here in the country now." After that Snorri died. He was sixty-seven years old at the time. That was one year after the fall of King Óláf the Saint, according to the priest Ari the Learned. Snorri was buried at Tunga, and Bolli and Thórdís took over the farm there, as Snorri had asked. Snorri's sons had no objection to this.

Bolli became a man of prominence and had many friends. Herdís Bolladóttir grew up at Helgafell and was a most beautiful woman. Orm, Hermund Illugason's son, asked for her hand and she was given to him in marriage. Their son was Kodrán, who later had Gudrún Sigmundardóttir as a wife. Kodrán's son was Hermund, and he was married to Úlfeid, the daughter of Rúnólf, son of Ketil the Bishop. Their sons were Rein, Kodrán, Styrmir, and Ketil who was an abbot at Helgafell. Their daughter was Thórver, who was married to Skeggi Brandsson, and from them have come the Skógar kin.

Bolli and Thórdís had a son whose name was Óspak. His daughter was Gudrún, who was married to Thórarin Brandsson. Their son was Brand who built the parsonage at Húsafell. His son was Sighvat the Priest who lived there a long time.

Gellir Thorkelsson took a wife. He married Valgerd, daughter of Thorgils Arason from Reykjanes. Gellir went abroad and was with King Magnús the Good and received as a gift from him twelve ounces of gold and many wares besides. Gellir's sons were Thorkel and Thorgils. Thorgils' son was Ari the Learned. The son of Ari was called Thorgils and his son was Ari the Strong.

Gudrún now began to grow very old and lived in such penance and grief as was told about a little while back. She was the first nun and hermitess in Iceland. It is commonly said that among women of equal birth, Gudrún was the noblest in the land. It is told how one time Bolli came to Helgafell to see her, and it always seemed very good to Gudrún when he came. He sat beside his mother for a long time, and they had much to talk about. Then Bolli said: "Will you tell me something, mother, that I have been curious to know? Which man did you love the most?" Gudrún answered: "Thorkel was the mightiest and the greatest chieftain, but no man was more accomplished or capable than Bolli. Thórd Ingunnarson was the wisest of them and the greatest lawspeaker. Thorvald I'll not even count." Then Bolli said: "I plainly see from what you are telling me how it was with each of your husbands, but still it remains unsaid which man you loved the most. There's no need for you to hide this any longer now." Gudrún answered: "You are pressing me hard, my son, but if I must tell this to anyone, then I'd rather have it be you." Bolli begged her to do so. Gudrún then spoke: "To him I was worst whom I loved most." "I think," said Bolli, "that the truth has now been told." And he said that she had done right to tell him what he so much wanted to know. Gudrún grew to be very old, and people say she became blind. She died at Helgafell and lies buried there.

Gellir Thorkelsson lived at Helgafell until old age and many remarkable things are told of him. He also comes into many of the sagas, although very little is said of him here. He had a very stately church built at Helgafell, as is confirmed in the memorial poem to Gellir which Arnór Jarlaskáld (Earl's Scald) composed and where he plainly states this. When Gellir was quite bowed down with advancing years, he set out from Iceland on a journey. He came to Norway, but did not stay long in that country, leaving soon for the south and continuing to Rome, where he visited the grave of the apostle Saint Peter. He stayed on this journey to the south a long time, and then came back to Denmark. There he took sick and lay abed for a long time and received all the last rites. Then he died and lies buried at Roskilde. Gellir had Skofnung with him, but it was never found afterwards. That sword had been taken from the mound of Hrólf Kraki.[1] When the news of Gellir's death reached Iceland, his son Thorkel took over the paternal inheritance at Helgafell. Thorgils, Gellir's other son, drowned as a youth in the Breidafjord, and all of those who had been on board with him. Thorkel Gellisson was a man of greatest worth and was said to be most learned. And here the saga ends.

Notes

INTRODUCTION

1. Parallels between the *Sturlunga saga* and *Laxdoela saga* were first noted by Kr. Kålund, *Aarbøger for nordisk oldkyndighed* (1901), p. 387; by Guð-brandur Vigfússon, *Origines Islandicae*, II (1905), 137; by Finnur Jónsson, *Litteratur historie* (2nd ed.; København, 1920-24) II, 551; by Andreas Heus-ler, *Deutsche Litteraturzeit* (1932), p. 2469. Einar Ó. Sveinsson, in his intro-duction to the *Laxdoela saga* (*Islenzk fornrit* [Reykjavík, 1934], V, xxxii-xxxiv) discusses those passages in *Laxdoela* that indicate the influence of *Sturlunga saga* and aid in dating the *Laxdoela*. Cf. also Einar Ó. Sveinsson, *Dating the Icelandic Sagas* (Viking Society for Northern Research, Vol. III; London: University College, 1958), p. 73. Rolf Heller has recently gathered together all the passages from the *Sturlunga saga* which exhibit striking parallels with *Laxdoela* and which must have influenced the author. Cf. Rolf Heller, "Lax-doela saga und Sturlunga saga," *Arkiv för nordisk filologi*, LXXVI (1961), 112-33.

2. Cf. *Þórðar saga kakala* in the *Sturlunga saga*, edited by Jón Jóhan-nesson, Magnús Finnbogason, and Kristján Eldjárn (Reykjavík, 1946), II, chapter clxxxiv (supplementary fragment), 283.

3. Cf. the article by Björn M. Ólsen, "Landnámabók und Laxdæla," *Aarbøger for nordisk oldkyndighed* (1908), pp. 151-232. The version used by the author of *Laxdoela* seems to have been an earlier redaction than the extant one of *Landnámabók*.

4. *Laxdoela* shows evidence that the author has been influenced by the Eddic poems, especially in the characters of the women — Melkorka, Thor-gerd, and Gudrún. There are also many thematic parallels (in some cases even in the very wording) between Brynhilde and Sigurd on the one hand and Gudrún and Kjartan on the other. But the Gudrún of the saga also re-flects the *Edda* Gudrún as well as Brynhilde. Association was probably made through the sameness of the names. This is also no doubt the case where the saga Gudrún has attracted the author to the Gudrún in *Guðmundar saga dýra* (in the *Sturlunga saga*), from which he assimilated some themes. Some of the more striking passages for comparison are: *Edda*, "Guðrúnarkviða I" (verses 9 and 10), and *Laxdoela* chapter 13, where Melkorka has been forced to serve the master and mistress of the house in the shoes and stockings

episode, and in the master's (Hoskuld's) relationship to the servant; *Edda,* "Grípisspá" (verse 53), and *Laxdoela* chapter 33, where Gudrún mentions that Gest could have given fairer prophecies if the dreams had so warranted; *Edda,* "Guðrúnarkviða II" (verse 30), and *Laxdoela* chapter 42, where Bolli says that Gudrún may be sitting some years husbandless; *Edda,* "Guðrúnarhvǫt" (verse 2), and *Laxdoela* chapter 48, where Gudrún eggs her brothers on to attack Kjartan; *Edda,* "Sigurðarkviða in skamma" (verse 30), and *Laxdoela* chapter 49, where Gudrún gloats over Hrefna's grief that she won't be going to bed laughing that night; *Edda,* "Sigurðarkviða in skamma" (verses 31 and 32), and *Laxdoela* chapter 49, where Bolli tells Gudrún that she wouldn't have turned less pale at the news that he (Bolli) had been killed instead of Kjartan; *Edda,* "Guðrúnarkviða I" (verse 1 and the refrain lines in verses 2, 5, and 11), and *Laxdoela* chapter 50, where it is stated that Hrefna died of a broken heart; *Edda,* "Brot Sigurðkviða" (verses 8 and 10), and *Laxdoela* chapter 55, where Thorgerd praises Steinthór for the "work of his hands" in killing Bolli.

5. A work as recent as Marco Scovazzi's *La Saga di Hrafnkell e il problema delle saghe islandesi* (Editrice Libreria Paideia, 1960) takes issue with Nordal's *Hrafnkatla* and reasserts the oral and historical origin of this saga.

6. Sigurður Nordal, *Hrafnkatla, Íslenzk fræði* 7 (Reykjavík, 1949). An English translation by R. George Thomas (Cardiff, 1958) has appeared under the title: *Hrafnkel's Saga Freysgoða: A Study.*

7. I refer the reader to my forthcoming publication, *The Structural and Formal Elements of the Laxdoela saga,* Vol. XL of *Islandica* (Cornell University Press).

CHAPTER 1

1. The title for such a local ruler was a *hersir.* It was used to describe certain local chieftains in Norway up to about 1150. It is not mentioned in the old laws and we have no sure idea of what the titleholder's functions and duties were. The title was inherited in some families.

2. The byname *Bjólan* is more than likely of Irish-Gaelic origin.

3. The byname *Hyrna* means "a female animal with horns, especially a ewe."

4. Óláf the White's genealogy as given here is more than likely incorrect. It has probably been confused and mixed with that of Helgi the Lean as given in the *Landnámabók.*

5. Fródi the Brave was a Danish king who was killed by an earl and his son, members of the Svertling family.

6. The byname *Manvitsbrekka* is compounded from *mannvit* meaning "sense" and *brekka* meaning "slope." Its meaning as a byname is obscure, but *brekka* is frequently used as a simile for "woman" in kennings.

7. *Kirkjubaer,* a locality in southern Iceland, is the modern Kirkjubæjarklaustur.

CHAPTER 2

1. The circumstances of Ketil's emigration from Norway are given somewhat differently in the *Eyrbyggja saga,* chapters i-iii, and v; and in the

Landnámabók, chapter lxiv. As nearly as one can figure, Bjorn went to Iceland ten years after Ingólf Arnarson had made the first settlement there. That would make it the year 884.

2. "West across the sea" means here "to the British Isles," that is, the land to the west of Norway.

3. The words "in his youth" have been inserted from MS E.

CHAPTER 3

1. The high-seat, *ǫndvegi,* was the seat of honor in the family dwelling. The posts of this seat, the *ǫndvegissúlur,* were ornamented with figureheads (usually of Thor) and with carvings and were regarded with religious reverence. Many of the settlers of Iceland are said to have taken the high-seat posts with them, and when nearing Iceland to have thrown them overboard to drift ashore. It was considered a good omen as to where they should set up their new home.

2. The reader is reminded that names ending in *-á* are river names.

CHAPTER 4

1. The reference is to Ari Thorgilsson the Learned, father of Icelandic history and author of the *Íslendingabók;* his dates are 1067-1148. It is probably no mere chance that the author invokes the authority of Ari here, and again near the end of the saga (chapter 78). This not only gives a clue to one of the author's sources, it puts the story in a historical framework, as if the author were appealing to the listeners and assuring them that what they are about to hear is a true and faithful account. Appeal to authority is one device to support a semblance of historicity.

2. Ketil Flatnose was also a *hersir,* cf. chapter 1, note 1.

3. The byname *Turf* was given to Einar in all likelihood because he used turf for fuel. Bynames frequently precede the personal name.

4. The name *Gotuskeggjar* denotes the people from a farm, *Gata,* in the Faroes. The noun *skeggi* is usually found in compounds and is often used to indicate islanders. *Skeggi* is related to the word *skegg,* "a beard" — thus perhaps these islanders were thought of as sturdy, bearded people. Compare also chapter 7 of the saga where the nickname *Mostrarskegg* is used of Thórólf from the island of Moster.

CHAPTER 5

1. The byname *Feilan* is no doubt the same as the Irish-Gaelic name *Faelan,* derived from *fael* meaning "wolf."

2. The name *Vikrarskeid* as such has not come down to the present day. It is probably the present name *Skeið* on the right bank of the Ölfúsá in the south of Iceland.

3. The explanation for the name is attributed to folk etymology, as are many other names in the saga such as Kambsnes (Comb's Ness), Kjalarey (Keel Island), Skjaldarey (Shield Island) and the like.

4. *Medalfellsstrond* is the strand at the mountain Medalfell on the northern side of the Hvammsfjord, the westernmost point of which is Dogurdarnes

Chapter 6

1. Hordadal is now called Horðudalur and is located on the south side of the Hvammsfjord.

2. *Ormstunga* is a byname meaning "snake's tongue." This is the Gunnlaug of the famous saga *Gunnlaugs saga ormstungu*.

3. The family and kin of the farm Gilsbakki.

4. Dala-Álf, that is Álf of the Dales. The Dales is a shortened form from Breidafjord Dales, which designates those valleys around the head of the Breidafjord (actually that arm of the Breidafjord called Hvammsfjord).

5. Thorstein's byname *Surt*, literally meaning "black," was also the name of a fire giant, the destroyer of the world, in the Eddic poems. Thorstein also bore the name *inn spaki*, "the Wise." The summer eke introduced by him was an intercalary week inserted every seventh year at the end of summer.

6. From the farm Hofdi in Eyjafjord.

Chapter 7

1. The byname *Kuggi* refers to a kind of ship, a *kuggr*, which is a word related to the English "cog." In all probability Thorkel owned such a ship.

2. The byname *Thorskabit* means literally "cod-fish biter," and is apparently used about a person who is an ardent fisherman.

3. Moster is an island off the coast of Norway. Cf. chapter 4, note 4.

4. *Godi*, a title used as a byname for a person who held the position of both temple priest and a chieftain in Iceland at the time of the Commonwealth when religious and political duties were closely associated. Cf. Introduction, p. xvi.

5. Tungu-Odd, that is "Odd from Tunga."

6. Herjólf was a *lendr maðr*, that is he held a fief of land directly from the king, a position corresponding approximately to the *hersir* of a still earlier time.

Chapter 8

1. The practice of sprinkling with water (*vatni ausinn*) was already a heathen custom and does not represent the influence of Christianity here. Later, after Christianization has taken place, the author is careful to make the distinction by employing the word for baptism: *skírask*. This indicates the author's endeavor to keep his story in its historical time. Although there are some anachronisms, he is for the most part very conscious of the time difference between the story he is telling and the time of writing it. He frequently points out such things as: "one can still see traces of it today," or "formerly there was a woods there." Cf. Introduction, p. xxii.

Chapter 9

1. Adalstein is the Anglo-Saxon king, Æthelstan, d. 940.

2. Jórunn's genealogy and marriage are reported differently in other sources. Even the references in the *Landnámabók* deviate from one another.

3. The Strands: this is the coastal stretch on the northeast side of the

large peninsula jutting out from Iceland's northwest corner. The district is
called Strandasýsla today.

4. The byname *Hólmgongu*-Bersi comes from the name for a duel originally fought on an islet or holm. Such a duel or wager differed from the
common duels, the *einvígi*, in that the former was governed by rites and
rules. Some of the champions of such wagers were nicknamed for their
participation.

CHAPTER 10

1. Víga-Hrapp has the same byname as Víga-Styr (Slayer-Styr) mentioned
in chapter 3.

2. The reference is to the passage where Thorstein Surt is mentioned
(chapter 6), although to be sure his homestead is not given there.

3. The byname *Trefil* means a "fringe," "fraying," or "rag," indicating a
person dressed in rags or tatters.

CHAPTER 11

1. The byname *Goddi* is likely a diminutive of *Godi*, "chieftain-priest."

2. The byname *Skrjúp* means "weak," or "frail," characteristics that are
later borne out. Thorbjorn and his son Lambi (cf. below, chapter 22) are
otherwise unattested.

3. *Vík* is the name given to the Oslofjord and its adjacent shores, in particular the east side. Here the Norwegian king had his residence at the time
of the saga.

CHAPTER 12

1. These islands are located near Gothenburg in Sweden, formerly a
point of intersection on the border between the three Scandinavian kingdoms,
and a lively trading center.

CHAPTER 13

1. In this connection the practice of name giving warrants special attention, for it carries with it not only social but religious significance. The
saga offers us several examples of children who were named for the deceased
father or relative (chapters 13, 28, 36, 47, 56, 78). The alternation of
names in any genealogical chart provides good evidence of the extent of the
practice in Iceland. Naturally this custom is not restricted to Iceland but
can be found elsewhere and continues to be a widespread convention today,
though much of the religious implications formerly attached to it has been
weakened or lost in our own day. In ancient Scandinavia, a person was
thought to have a spiritual double that accompanied him throughout life.
This *fylgja* (fetch) was sometimes visible to those with second sight. Thorgils Holluson meets his *fylgja* on the way to the Althing (chapter 67). She
appears as an unusually large woman and turns away from the Thing as
Thorgils is on his way there — foreboding his death. When a person died,
his *fylgja* could be transferred to a new-born infant by giving the child the
name of the deceased. The *fylgja* went with the name, and in this manner

the deceased also gained some sort of immortality. It was generally hoped that the name would have the power to invest the child with the same qualities inherent in the former bearer of the name. Víga-Hrapp in our story has a namesake near the end of the saga who declares that he has all the characteristics of the former Víga-Hrapp and all that the name implies, that is, a great warrior and "slayer" (chapter 63).

Chapter 14

1. The saga exhibits a mixture of past and present tenses throughout the narrative, shifting sometimes within the same sentence. The reader is never disoriented as to the time of the action however. This shifting would seem to indicate the well-known device of a historical present to liven up the action, but in the case of *Laxdoela* it may also well point to the author's amalgamation of time past and time present, cf. Introduction, pp. xvi, xxii, xxxvii. Generally I have leveled out the text in favor of the narrative past, using the present only occasionally to brighten an episode and give some of the flavor of the original.

Chapter 16

1. The text actually reads: "You shall now also know for what reward you have worked." The author seems to have forgotten that Ásgaut has already been told this, cf. chapter 15.

2. Cf. chapter 11, when all the neighbors and Thórd come to Hoskuld for protection against Hrapp.

Chapter 17

1. Icelandic farmhouses were built in series, small buildings joined together, with each little house corresponding to a room used for a specific purpose. The *eldhús,* literally "firehouse," was the kitchen where the fire was kept up and the family gathered.

Chapter 18

1. The Kolkistustraum is thought to be the same as the present-day Kollköstungur, and is a strait between the mainland and the Ólafseyjar in the Hvammsfjord. The current and waters are particularly treacherous.

2. According to folklore if one were bewitched and changed into another shape, the eyes were believed to remain the same. The seal here is, of course, Víga-Hrapp, who has not given up his hauntings and is keeping "his eye" out for his farm — for after all Thorstein is on his way there to take over the deserted farmstead. We know from the hint in chapter 17 that Hrapp's hauntings are not completely over: "Hrapp's hauntings more or less let up." This "more or less" (*heldr*) is one of the many subtleties of the text. That Thorstein was beset with such difficulties not only is explainable on the natural level, a supernatural force also played its role.

3. This sentence seems to give the final result of the case about the drownings, which immediately follows. The author anticipates himself and then proceeds to tell how it all happened that way.

4. Such ordeals are mentioned in former times as proof of guilt or innocence, especially when it was difficult to get any other means of proof. It was also used in swearing oaths of brotherhood: *Gísla saga,* chapter vi; *Fóstbraeðra saga,* chapter ii. Sometimes it was used as a disgrace: *Vatnsdaela saga,* chapter xxxiii; *Njáls saga,* chapter cxix.

5. This sentence is meant ironically as an introduction to Thorkel's next subterfuge. It is typical understatement in saga style. It is true, of course, that the continuity of thought is interrupted, for the author puts in an aside, comparing heathen and Christian attitudes toward ordeals, cf. Introduction, p. xxii.

6. It was common practice for the ordeal to be taken by proxy; this is therefore not another trick on Thorkel's part.

CHAPTER 19

1. There is some confusion in the MSS about the name Kambsnes and the farm there, cf. below, chapter 20.

2. The use of the word "thralls" in the text here does not mean that the housecarls and the slaves were of the same status. Hrút is using "thralls" as a derogatory designation for Hoskuld's housecarls, who generally represented both freedmen and bondmen.

3. Jórunn is comparing Hrút to a *hornungr,* originally meaning an illegitimate child. Such children, born out of wedlock as Hoskuld's son Óláf (cf. chapter 26 below), were likely to be cheated out of any due share when the father's inheritance was settled.

4. The story of these quarrels is told at the beginning of the *Njáls saga.* Hrút goes to Norway after his betrothal to Unn, but when he returns and marries, he finds that Queen Gunnhild has bewitched him. This ruins his marriage and Unn divorces him. Later she inveigles Gunnar of Fljótshlíd to get her dowry money back from Hrút.

5. The *Landnámabók* names altogether twenty children for Hrút.

CHAPTER 20

1. The explanation for this statement and Thorleik's move to Kambsnes does not come until chapter 25. It is also to be noted that the author has brought old age upon Hoskuld sowewhat prematurely, in view of all the intervening events before chapter 26 when the thread is picked up again concerning Hoskuld's illness and death.

2. Lambastadir is Thorbjorn Skrjúp's farmstead, although it could not have got this name until after Lambi, the son of Thorbjorn and Melkorka, took it over (cf. below, chapter 38). The author has failed to put himself back into the time of the story and has used the name it had later.

3. Thirty hundreds is equal to approximately 3,600 ells of woollen frieze or *vadmal.* The hundred is the "long" hundred, that is one hundred and twenty. Hereafter whenever the figure hundred is mentioned in the saga, the "long" hundred should be understood.

4. The teething gift, *tannfé,* was a gift to an infant upon cutting its first tooth — a custom still observed in Iceland today.

CHAPTER 21

1. "West across the sea" is again to the British Isles.

2. Just as the *fylgja* was thought to be transferable (chapter 13, note 1), so too were *hamingja* and *gipta*, the spirits of good luck. These latter however could also be transferred during one's life time, as we see here and in chapter 26 where Hoskuld bequeaths to Óláf all the family's *gipta*.

3. Trading vessels often had an interpreter along, and we must remember that Melkorka has taught Óláf Irish as if in anticipation of this. The author does not fail to use all the strands of his narrative.

4. This spear is also described in the text by the word *hǫggtekit*, which appears to be a *hapax legomenon* of obscure meaning, and I have left it out in the translation. In MSS M and E and in many paper MSS the word is written as *hauggtekit*, that is, "taken from a burial mound, *haugr*." MS V has *haugrekin* (same as *hǫggrekin*, "inlaid, chased"). It is interesting to note that the sword Skofnung (chapters 57 and 78) had been taken from a *haugr*, the mound of Hrólf Kraki in Denmark.

CHAPTER 22

1. Skalla-Grím, the affixed byname *skalli*, literally "skull," often seems to mean "bald-headed." This is the famous Egil of *Egils saga*.

CHAPTER 23

1. The version followed here is taken from zpap. which attributes the phrase to Egil instead of Hoskuld.

2. From the number of passages in the saga that assume that the wedding feast is at the groom's farmstead, this would not seem to signify any special honor: cf. chapters 7, 9, 20, 23 (here), 24, 45.

CHAPTER 24

1. Haugsgard, a fence or wall (*garðr*) enclosing a burial mound (*haugr*).

2. Hoskuldsstadir lies on the south side of the Laxá opposite Hjardarholt. Hoskuld and Jórunn can therefore stand outside their farm and easily watch Óláf move from Goddastadir. Cf. map, p. xlv.

3. The name Hjardarholt meaning "Herdholt" refers to the fact that Óláf's cattle used to gather there in the woods or "holt."

CHAPTER 25

1. This paragraph about Hoskuld's sons seeems to take up the thread of chapter 9 — what happened after Thorleik and Bárd grew up — and to precede the events of chapter 20. The author's method of backtracking is generally more skillfully done. The opening paragraph of chapter 20 and all of chapter 25 are obviously meant to supplement one another.

2. The division of the property between Hoskuld and Hrút after the settlement of their mother's inheritance likely led to Hrút's leaving his farm

at Kambsnes (elsewhere attested as Bólstad) and moving to Hrútsstadir. He no doubt settled the freedman down somewhere near his old farm.

3. From the inner coherency of the saga itself, it would seem that the property must have been held jointly by Hoskuld and Thorleik at the time Hrút settled the freedman down there. Later Hoskuld paid out to Thorleik his share of the family property when he wanted to marry.

CHAPTER 26

1. The twelve ounces, *tólf aurar*, were the legally fixed sum that could be given an illegitimate child. But the *eyrir* (pl. *aurar*) used as a unit of value was calculated as an ounce of *silver*. Thus the legal twelve ounces were to be so interpreted here, but by subreption Hoskuld deceives his legitimate sons by giving Óláf the equivalent weight in gold. The ratio of value between gold and silver was something like eight or ten to one.

CHAPTER 29

1. Hordaland is a district in southwest Norway. Cf. chapter 11, where it is stated that Bergen is "now" (at the time of composition) in that area.

CHAPTER 31

1. The byname *Smith* indicated a craftsman in general, not merely a worker in metals.
2. The name Harri is often found in the language of the scalds and means "lord, chieftain, king."
3. The *brunnvaka* was Harri's special horn that he used for an ice pick to chop open the frozen watering holes.

CHAPTER 32

1. The famous conqueror of Normandy. His byname *Gongu-Hrólf* or "Walking-Hrólf," is attributed to the fact that he was so heavy that no horse could carry him.
2. The *Landnámabók* has no record of a Thórir the Wealthy (*Þórir sælingr*), but a *Þórarinn sælingr*. The byname *sælingr* means both "an epicurean" and "a wealthy, lucky man."

CHAPTER 33

1. There is frequent mention in Old Icelandic writings of hot springs, *laugar*, from which the farm at *Laugar* in Saelingsdal got its name. These springs were used for bathing and washing of clothes, and usually a house or shed was built over such a spring.
2. The phrase literally means "cast into the sea" (*á sæ kastat*) and originally was used about casting nets in vain, getting nothing in return. Then figuratively came to mean "squander, waste."
3. The "helmet of terror" or *ægishjálmr* is a helmet capable of striking terror and fright into the heart of another, figuratively used of one who holds another in subjection or fear. It occurs in many Old Icelandic sources, notably in the *Edda*.

CHAPTER 34

1. The period from approximately the middle of August to the middle of September.

2. This shirt with "a wide neck opening" is literally called a shirt with "a divorce head hole" in the saga. It was cut so low that the breast nipples showed. A husband who wore such a shirt apparently could be legally divorced by his wife. In the following chapter we have the corresponding case of a woman who was divorced for wearing clothes unbefitting to a woman.

CHAPTER 35

1. The little alliterative verse appears to be a quotation from a lost poem:
> Vel er ek veit þat,
> vask ein of látin.

2. The shiel (*sel*) was a cabin or shed like the Norwegian *sæter* which served as an outlying dairy or herder's hut during the summer. It was normally located up in the mountains or hills where there was summer pasture, and was quite some distance from the winter quarters or main farm.

3. There were several degrees of outlawry. In this case Thórd asks for *skóggangr*, which implied that the offender was banished to the woods (*skógr*). He was thus outside the pale of the law and it was felony to shelter or aid such an outlaw in any way.

CHAPTER 36

1. A favorite sport in old Norway and Iceland. The horses were goaded on to fight with their forelegs and teeth. Not infrequently their owners came to blows themselves.

CHAPTER 37

1. The belief in the "evil eye" was widespread in Scandinavia. It has all but disappeared, however, in Iceland today. The evil eye could bring about ill luck, make people go mad, or turn the lay of the land inside out (cf. next chapter).

2. The Icelandic proverb implies that one will run up against some obstacle or force and not be able to proceed any further: "force will meet force."

CHAPTER 38

1. Götaland, the southern part of Sweden.

CHAPTER 40

1. The byname *Skokul* is of uncertain meaning; literally it means "pole of a wagon, or its shaft," and may be used as a phallic symbol.

2. Bishop Ísleif (1006-80) was the first bishop of Iceland and had his see at Skálholt.

3. It is told below how he came by his nickname.

4. All the MSS have Fljótshlíd here, but Breidá was a farm in the district Fellshverfi in southeastern Iceland.

5. Cf. chapter 21, note 2.

6. The holiest festival was Easter.

7. This was done one week after baptism.

8. Because of Scald Hallfred's stubborn insistence on this he was nicknamed "The Difficult Scald."

CHAPTER 41

1. Sídu-Hall, that is Hall from the district of Sída.

CHAPTER 43

1. The Winter Nights designates the time around the middle of October and the beginning of winter.

2. The king is using the Icelandic word *ráðakostr* with both its connotations: "station in life," and "marriage."

3. The wedding gift called the "bench gift" was given to the bride while she was sitting on the bride's bench at the wedding.

CHAPTER 44

1. The saga is not accurate here, for the scarlet clothes were given to Kjartan after his refusal to go to Iceland to convert his kinsmen (chapter 41). Kjartan received a sword from the king at parting (chapter 43).

2. This sword, *Konungsnaut*, literally meaning "the king's gift," will be called by its Icelandic epithet throughout this translation; for it, like Footbite, plays a special role and must be distinguished from other "king's gifts" in the saga.

3. Ordinary clothing was of undyed homespun, thus colored clothing was considered a luxury and worthy of note.

CHAPTER 45

1. Iceland was (and still is) divided into four geographical and political quarters: the *Nordlendingafjórðungr*, the *Sunnlendingafjórðungr*, the *Vestlendingafjórðungr*, and the *Austlendingafjórðungr* (the North, South, West, and East Quarters, respectively).

2. "Dry fast" or *þurr matr* consisted of dried fish and bread with no butter, meat, or milk products.

CHAPTER 47

1. This homespun (*vadmal*, English "wadmal") was of a certain high quality and had a fixed value on the market.

CHAPTER 48

1. Sveinsson in his edition has selected the word *trog*, "trough," from a zpap. MS, whereas MS M has here *hrís*, "brushwood." This scene in the

dream is typical of the appearance of troll women. The *skálm*, "stubby sword or knife," the brushwood, and the trough are all part of the paraphernalia of the folklore motif.

CHAPTER 49

1. The text has been corrected here, for it reads that there were *six* to Kjartan's and Án's two; whereas one of Ósvíf's sons (Thórólf) has been put out of the fight. A little further on the saga author correctly mentions *four* sons of Ósvíf participating in the fight, not all five.

2. I have used the version of the text found in MS M, which reads: "'mikil verða hermðarverk, ek hefi spunnit tólf alna garn, en þú hefir vegit Kjartan'" (*Laxdoela Saga*, edited by Kr. Kålund [København, 1889-91], p. 192). Sveinsson has used zpap. 226 instead: "'Misjofn verða morginverkin; ek hefi spunnit...'" (E. Ó. Sveinsson edition of the saga, p. 154). The word *hermðarverk* is a *hapax legomenon* and therefore can only be interpreted from this one context: an activity which is the fruit of dissatisfaction or embitterment (cf. J. Fritzner, *Ordbog over det gamle norske sprog*). MS zpap. 226 and MS M elucidate one another and aid in the interpretation of the text. The morning's tasks (*morginverk*) not only are unequal (*misjofn*), both grew out of dissatisfaction and embitterment. Gudrún, nurturing her discontent and embitterment, goaded Bolli into killing Kjartan. Under the strain of waiting for the outcome, she takes to some activity — a frantic spinning (undoubtedly twelve ells represent a great deal in a short time). Thus both activities are "mikil." The tension which her spinning represents is heightened by the fact that she may be hoping against hope that it is Bolli that is slain. Bolli hints as much when he returns from the battle. Bolli for his part also undertook the deed out of dissatisfaction and embitterment, for he finally let his envy of Kjartan get the better of him.

CHAPTER 51

1. Payment for passage had to be given, for otherwise it was unlawful to transport an outlawed person.

2. Ósvíf mocks him by using his byname disparagingly.

CHAPTER 54

1. MS zpap. 226 is followed here for the order of the listing.

CHAPTER 55

1. Most of these place names have not survived into modern times, although their locations can be pointed out if one wanders through Saelingsdal.

2. The phrase comes almost as an anticipated refrain for the reader; I have thus inserted it here from MS M. Sveinsson omits it in his edition.

CHAPTER 56

1. The *Eyrbyggjar* were the people from Eyr (now Hallbjarnareyri), a farm in the west. Their story is told in the *Eyrbyggja saga*.

Chapter 57

1. The sword Skofnung had been owned by King Hrólf Kraki as is later told in chapter 78. Midfjardar-Skeggi supposedly took it from his burial mound. The condition that no sun was to shine on its hilt is in accordance with many ancient superstitions and precautions. (Cf. the Eggjum stone in Norway.)

2. A chain of lakes especially noted for their good fishing.

Chapter 58

1. The idiom used here is *snarisk í bragð*, literally "snared into a plan, trick or scheme." Thorkel naturally is thinking in general, practical terms that more and bigger men will have to be brought into any plan for Bolli's revenge. It is essential that the reader sense the primary meaning of the idiom, for it is by a trick, indeed by two tricks, that Snorri accomplishes his objective, and it is none other than Thorgils who is snared. The two levels are intended for a "double audience" — the general meaning as far as Thorgils knows, and the specific meaning in Snorri's mind, directed to the reader. Later, in the ditty spoken by the cloak (chapter 67), the word *bragð* comes up again. The reader is thus prepared here for the action that spans the whole next section.

Chapter 59

1. This crag is now called Gálghamar.

2. Snorri uses the word *samlendr maðr*, which carries a duplicity of meaning: "a countryman, that is from the same country, but also in the country at the same time." Snorri's first "trick" thus hinges on a wile, a scheme within a scheme.

Chapter 60

1. Older sources offer little support to the statement that common farms such as this had vegetable gardens.

Chapter 65

1. "Helmet's tree," a kenning for warrior.

Chapter 66

1. This passage is probably meant to foretell the founding of a monastery at Helgafell which took place in 1184.

2. Cf. above, chapter 33.

Chapter 67

1. The epithet is *Holluslappi*, literally "Halla's Lanky Lubber."

2. This saga has been lost.

Chapter 68

1. The benches were situated lengthwise along the side walls of the hall. The high-seats were in the middle of the benches. The higher or first high-seat was in the middle of the bench which faced toward the sun or south. On the opposite side, facing north, was the lower bench.

Chapter 69

1. Gunnar is also told about in the *Droplaugarsonasaga*, in *Fljótsdoela þáttr* and especially in *Gunnars þáttr*. The *Njarðvíkingasaga* mentioned here is in all likelihood this *þáttr*.

Chapter 73

1. Sarpsborg was the royal residence at Vík on the east side of the Oslofjord.

2. Miklagard, "the Great Stronghold," is the Icelandic name for Constantinople.

3. Bolli became a member of the Varangian guard at the imperial court in Constantinople. The term *Væringjar* was first used for the Scandinavian settlers in Russia. Later it was applied to the Viking warriors in the service of the emperor of Constantinople. The word itself is probably derived from *várar*, "oaths of allegiance." The Varangians then were those bound by such oaths. Obviously Bolli Bollason could not have been the first Norseman to enter this service. The author merely enhances Bolli's pomp and glory in this way.

Chapter 74

1. The idiom used is *drepa skeggi*, literally meaning "to dip or immerse one's beard" and figuratively used with the meaning "to drown." Taking up the symbol of the dream, Gudrún uses it both humorously in its literal sense and seriously as a portent of what is to come (cf. her fourth dream).

Chapter 75

1. Halldór has spoken his threat almost as a curse, therefore he deserves equally bad treatment.

2. It is Lent.

Chapter 76

1. That there were twelve on board is taken from MS C.

2. King Óláf the Saint fell at Stiklestad in Norway in the year 1030.

Chapter 77

1. The description of Footbite in MS M for this passage is not in agreement with that one given in chapter 29 above, where the sword is said to have had no chased work but a walrus tusk for a hilt. The variant in MS zpap. 226, which is used in this translation, aids in a plausible explanation, for the added word *nú* ("now") points up the author's consciousness of the change in the sword — which is not at all surprising in view of the enhancement of all of Bolli's accoutrements.

Chapter 78

1. Hrólf Kraki is a legendary Danish king from the sixth century. It is therefore not surprising that the sword "disappears," as in folklore tradition.